C000217991

Maths

Rapid Tests 3

Rebecca Brant

Schofield & Sims

Introduction

This book gives you practice in answering mathematics questions quickly.

The questions are like the questions on the 11+ and other school selection tests. You must find the correct answers.

School selection tests are usually timed, so you need to get used to working quickly. Each test has a target time for you to work towards. You should time how long you spend on each test, or you can ask an adult to time you.

What you need

- A pencil
- An eraser
- A ruler
- A clock, watch or stopwatch
- A sheet of rough paper
- An adult to help you work out how long you take and to mark the test for you

What to do

- Turn to **Section 1 Test 1** on page 4. Look at the grey box at the top of the page labelled **Target time**. This tells you how long the test should take.
- When you are ready to start, write down the time or start the stopwatch. Or the adult helping you will tell you to begin.
- Read each question carefully and then write the answer on the answer line. Sometimes you need to draw your answer in the space instead. You should not use a calculator.
- Try to answer every question. If you do get stuck on a question, leave it and go on to the next one. Work quickly and try your best.
- When you reach the end, stop. Write down the time or stop the stopwatch. Or tell the adult that you have finished.
- With the adult, work out how long you took to do the test. Fill in the **Time taken** box at the end of the test.
- The adult will mark your test and fill in the **Score** and **Target met?** boxes.
- Turn to the **Progress chart** on page 40. Write your score in the box and colour in the graph to show how many questions you got right.
- Did you get some questions wrong? You should always have another go at them before you look at the answers. Then ask the adult to check your work and help you if you are still not sure.
- Later, you will do some more of these tests. You will soon learn to work through them more quickly. The adult who is helping you will tell you what to do next.

Published by **Schofield & Sims Ltd**,
7 Mariner Court, Wakefield, West Yorkshire WF4 3FL, UK
Telephone 01484 607080
www.schofieldandsims.co.uk

This edition copyright © Schofield & Sims Ltd, 2018
First published in 2018

Author: **Rebecca Brant**. Rebecca Brant has asserted her moral rights under the Copyright, Designs and Patents Act, 1988, to be identified as the author of this work.

British Library Cataloguing in Publication Data. A catalogue record for this book is available from the British Library.

All rights reserved. No part of this publication may be reproduced, stored in a retrieval system, or transmitted in any form or by any means, electronic, mechanical, photocopying, recording or otherwise, without either the prior permission of the publisher or a licence permitting restricted copying in the United Kingdom issued by the Copyright Licensing Agency Limited, Barnard's Inn, 86 Fetter Lane, London EC4A 1EN.

Design by **Ledgard Jepson Ltd**
Front cover design by **Ledgard Jepson Ltd**
Printed in the UK by **Page Bros (Norwich) Ltd**

ISBN 978 07217 1423 3

Contents

A **pull-out answers section** (pages A1 to A16) appears in the centre of this book, between pages 20 and 21. It also gives simple guidance on how best to use this book. Remove this section before the child begins working through the tests.

Target time: **12 minutes**

1. Complete these sequences.

    a) 36, 42, 48, _____, _____, 66

    b) 14, 21, 28, _____, _____, 49

2. What is the value of each underlined digit?

    a) 4739 _____

    b) 2846 _____

3. Write the number that is 1000 more.

    _____

4. Write the number that is 1000 less.

    _____

5. Write **<** or **>** to make these statements correct.

    a) 345 _____ 354

    b) 738 _____ 729

6. Write these numbers in descending order.

1320		1203
	123	
321		1302

    _____

7. Write these numbers in ascending order.

    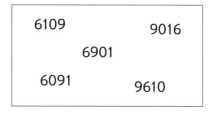

6109		9016
	6901	
6091		9610

    _____

8. Round these numbers to the nearest 10.

    a) 46 _____

    b) 91 _____

9. Round these numbers to the nearest 100.

    a) 97 _____

    b) 245 _____

10. Molly thinks of a number that has 3 thousands, 4 hundreds, 4 tens and 8 units. Ali's number is 2 hundreds less. What is Ali's number? _____

11. Naadiya thinks of a number that has 4 thousands, 9 hundreds, 2 tens and 5 units. Leo's number is 3 thousands more. What is Leo's number? _____

12. Write these Roman numerals in digits.

    a) XXII _____

    b) XXXVI _____

13. Estimate the numbers on the number line.

    0   a)   b)   1000

    a) _____   b) _____

Score: _____ **Time taken:** _____ **Target met?** _____

Target time: **12 minutes**

1. Use column addition to solve these calculations.

   a) 264 + 132 =

   b) 516 + 281 =

2. Use column subtraction to solve these calculations.

   a) 487 − 235 =

   b) 585 − 412 =

3. Tamara had 97 marbles. She swapped 28 for some stickers and another seventeen for some gel pens. How many marbles does she have left? _____

4. Sammy has 123 conkers and Tilly has 46 more than Sammy. How many do they have altogether? _____

5. Nora's swimming club had 137 members. Fifty-two were boys, forty-eight were girls and the rest were adults. How many were adults? _____

6. Harry had 196 football cards. He lost 37. How many was he left with? _____

7. The school secretary ordered 376 pencils. She gave 57 to Class 4GH and 66 to Class 4RS. How many pencils did the secretary have left? _____

8. Solve these calculations.

   a) 8 × 7 = _____

   b) 9 × 3 = _____

   c) 132 ÷ 11 = _____

   d) 72 ÷ 9 = _____

   e)
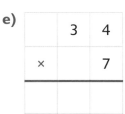

   f)
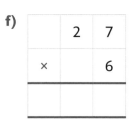

9. Henhouses can hold twelve chickens. If there are 8 henhouses, how many chickens will they be able to hold altogether? _____

10. There are 135 sweets in a jar. How many sweets will there be in 6 jars? _____

11. If there were 31 children in each class, how many children would there be in 8 classes? _____

12. In a packet of sunflower seeds, there are 82 seeds. If Paul buys 4 packets, how many seeds will he have? _____

13. Each school coach seats 64 children. On a school trip, Year 4 filled 3 coaches. How many children were going on the trip? _____

Score:		Time taken:		Target met?	

1. Write the equivalent fractions shown by the shaded areas.

   a)

   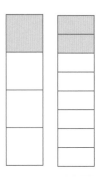

   _____ = _____

   b)

   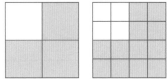

   _____ = _____

2. Complete these equivalent fractions.

   a) $\frac{1}{2} = \frac{?}{6}$ _____

   b) $\frac{1}{2} = \frac{?}{10}$ _____

3. Find these numbers.

   a) What is $\frac{1}{4}$ of 24? _____

   b) What is $\frac{1}{3}$ of 18? _____

   c) What is $\frac{1}{10}$ of 360? _____

   d) What is $\frac{1}{100}$ of 2300? _____

4. Solve these fractions sums.

   a) $\frac{3}{10} + \frac{4}{10} =$ _____

   b) $\frac{4}{9} + \frac{2}{9} =$ _____

   c) $\frac{6}{7} - \frac{3}{7} =$ _____

   d) $\frac{4}{8} - \frac{1}{8} =$ _____

5. Joshua spent $\frac{1}{3}$ of the day sleeping. How many hours was he awake? _____

6. Hayley spent $\frac{1}{4}$ of her pocket money on a new notepad.

   50p

   If the notepad cost 50p, how much pocket money did she start with? _____

7. Write these fractions as decimals.

   a) $\frac{1}{10}$ _____

   b) $\frac{4}{10}$ _____

8. Round these decimals to the nearest whole number.

   a) 3.7 _____

   b) 4.5 _____

9. A can of lemonade holds 0.25l. How much would 5 cans hold in litres? _____

10. Charlotte bought 2.3kg of raisins. She made six fruitcakes for her friends, using 0.3kg of raisins in each cake. What weight of raisins did she have left? _____

Score: _____ **Time taken:** _____ **Target met?** _____

1. Complete the table.

Grams (g)	Kilograms (kg) and grams (g)	Fraction (kg)	Decimal (kg)
500g	0kg 500g	$\frac{1}{2}$ kg	0.5kg
800g		$\frac{8}{10}$ kg	
	1kg 200g		1.2kg

2. The clock on Jamal's wall is an analogue clock. His alarm clock is a 12-hour digital clock. Write the times on his alarm clock, based on the times on his wall clock. Both of these times are in the afternoon.

a)

b)
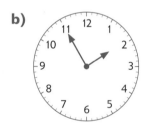 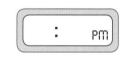

3. Tolu is 8 years and 7 months old. How many months old in total is she? _____

4. Tony has 3 dogs. Write each dog's height in centimetres.

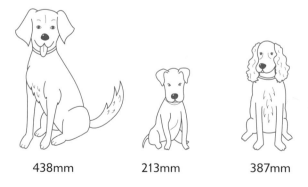

438mm   213mm   387mm

a) _____ cm b) _____ cm c) _____ cm

5. Calculate the perimeter of these shapes.

a)
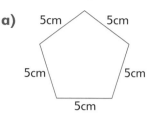
5cm 5cm
5cm 5cm
5cm
_____ cm

b)
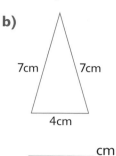
7cm 7cm
4cm
_____ cm

c)
12cm
5cm
_____ cm

6. Marco buys a banana for 30p, an apple for 15p and an orange for 20p.

a) How much money does he spend? _____

b) What change does he get from £2? _____

7. Ella buys 2 pencils costing 35p each, and a pen costing 50p.

a) How much does she spend? _____

b) She takes a £1 coin from her purse. How much more money does she need to get out? _____

8. How much liquid is in each container?

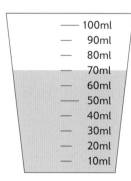

a) _____ ml   b) _____ ml

c) What is the difference between the two volumes? _____ ml

Score:		Time taken:		Target met?	

Target time: **12 minutes**

1. Draw the line of symmetry on each shape.

a)

b)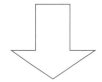

c)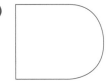

d)

2. Reflect the shape in the mirror line.

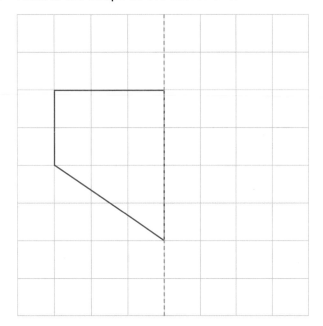

3. Label these angles **acute**, **obtuse** or a **right angle**.

a) _____

b) _____

c) _____

4. Complete the table to show the number of pairs of parallel sides in these quadrilaterals.

Quadrilateral	Number of pairs of parallel sides
Square	
Rectangle	
Trapezium	
Kite	
Rhombus	
Parallelogram	

5. Write the positions of the following shapes.

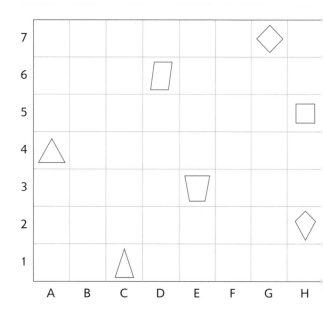

Example Square

a) Rhombus _____

b) Trapezium _____

c) Equilateral triangle _____

d) Kite _____

e) Parallelogram _____

f) Isosceles triangle _____

Score: _____   Time taken: _____   Target met? _____

Target time: **12 minutes**

1. Five school football teams played each other in the autumn term.

Longhorn vs Claremont	Gamble vs Stratton	Claremont vs St. John's	Longhorn vs St. John's
St. John's vs Stratton	Claremont vs Stratton	St. John's vs Longhorn	Claremont vs Gamble
St. John's vs Gamble	Stratton vs Longhorn	Gamble vs Longhorn	Stratton vs Gamble
Stratton vs Claremont	Gamble vs St. John's	Claremont vs Longhorn	St. John's vs Claremont

a) Use the information to complete the tally chart below, showing the number of games played by each team.

Team	Tally	Total
Longhorn		
Gamble		
Claremont		
Stratton		
St. John's		

b) Use the tally chart to complete the bar chart.

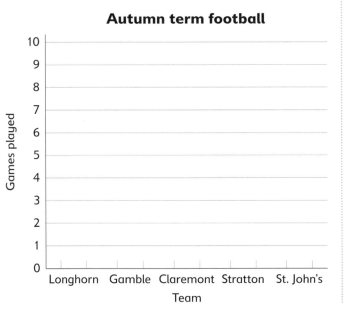

Autumn term football

2. Verity noticed that the temperature in May was very changeable. One day, she decided to monitor the temperature over the course of 7 hours. The line graph below shows her results.

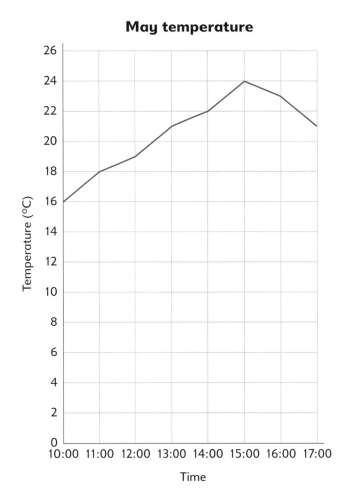

a) At what time was it the coolest? _____

b) At what time was it the warmest? _____

c) The temperature at 13:00 was 21°C. At what other time was the temperature the same? _____

d) How long did it take for the temperature to rise from 19°C to 24°C? _____

e) At what time did the temperature start to drop? _____

Score:		Time taken:		Target met?	

Target time: **12 minutes**

1. Elsa made 235 iced biscuits for a wedding. One hundred and twelve were pink, eighty-seven were blue and the rest were green. How many green biscuits were there? _____

2. A local café bought a box of five hundred tea bags. If they used ninety-six tea bags on Monday and one hundred and thirty-four on Tuesday, how many tea bags were left for the rest of the week? _____

3. Write these numbers in descending order.

   4632   4263   3462   6246   2634

   _____

4. Write each number in words.

   a) 948

   _____

   b) 1004

   _____

5. Deepak baked 144 cookies for a bake sale. He shared them between 12 plates. How many cookies did he place on each plate? _____

6. Ellie displayed her thirty-two ornaments on four shelves. How many were on each shelf? _____

7. Find these numbers.

   a) What is $\frac{1}{5}$ of 20? _____

   b) What is $\frac{1}{4}$ of 36? _____

   c) What is $\frac{1}{6}$ of 42? _____

8. Claire had 30 stickers. She gave away $\frac{1}{10}$ of them. How many did she keep? _____

9. Write these times on the 12-hour digital clocks. Both of these times are in the morning. Remember to use **a.m.** or **p.m.**

   a)

   b)
   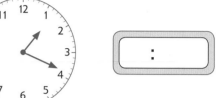

10. Sam and his family arrive at the zoo at 10:00 a.m. They spend 4 hours looking at the animals before they leave to go home. At what time do they leave? _____

11. Convert these measurements.

    a) 1.4l = _____ ml

    b) 1600m = _____ km

    c) 5200ml = _____ l

    d) 1.3km = _____ m

12. Calculate the perimeter of these shapes.

    a)
    22cm
    9cm
    _____

    b)
    12cm
    14cm
    _____

Score: _____   Time taken: _____   Target met? _____

Target time: **12 minutes**

1. Calculate the perimeter of this shape.

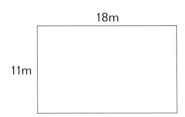

18m

11m

_____m

2. The perimeter of a square is 36cm. How long is each side? _____

3. Sarah's pet snake is 360mm long. How long is it in centimetres? _____

4. Lauren weighs 33kg with her school rucksack on and 28kg without her rucksack on. How much does her rucksack weigh? _____kg

5. Use column subtraction and addition to solve these calculations.

a) 345 + 187 =   b) 765 − 416 =

6. Name these shapes.

a) _____   b) _____

 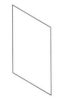

c) _____   d) _____

7. Complete these equivalent fractions.

a) $\frac{1}{2} = \frac{?}{12}$ _____

b) $\frac{1}{2} = \frac{?}{16}$ _____

c) $\frac{1}{4} = \frac{?}{8}$ _____

d) $\frac{1}{4} = \frac{?}{24}$ _____

8. In class 4A there are six hundred and twenty-nine fiction books. There are 245 on the top shelf of the bookcase and 213 on the bottom shelf. How many books are on the middle shelf? _____

9. The children at Ashdown School went shopping in the school shop.

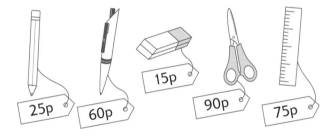

25p   60p   15p   90p   75p

a) Lyla bought 2 pens, a pencil and a pair of scissors. How much did she spend? _____

b) Melissa bought a pen, a ruler and an eraser. What was her change from £2? _____

c) Tyler had £3. He bought 3 pencils and an eraser. How much did he have left? _____

d) Emma needed to buy a pair of scissors, a ruler and a new pen. She only had £2. How much extra did she need? _____

e) Ashad bought two different items and spent £1.50. Which two items did he buy?

_____

| Score: | | Time taken: | | Target met? | |

Target time: **12 minutes**

1. Write the equivalent fractions shown by the shaded areas.

 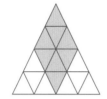

 = _____

2. Complete these equivalent fractions.

   a) $\frac{1}{3} = \frac{?}{9}$ _____

   b) $\frac{1}{5} = \frac{?}{10}$ _____

   c) $\frac{1}{6} = \frac{?}{24}$ _____

3. Complete these sequences.

   a) 45, 54, _____, _____, 81, 90

   b) _____, 28, _____, 42, 49, 56

4. Write these numbers in digits.

   a) Six hundred and thirty-nine   _____

   b) One thousand, two hundred and seventy-four   _____

5. Nial has a piece of wood 4.8m long. Avi has a piece of wood that is 1.3m longer. How long is Avi's piece of wood?   _____

6. Jug A contains 4.6l of water. Jug B contains 1.9l less. How much water does Jug B contain?   _____

7. Write two factor pairs for the number 12.

   a) _____ and _____

   b) _____ and _____

8. Convert these measurements.

   a) 4.7kg = _____ g

   b) 1600g = _____ kg

9. Draw the hands on the clocks so they show the correct time.

   a) **07:24**

   b) **04:13**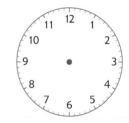

10. The pictogram shows how much money Grace saved over a 6-week period.

    £2 = £2

    | Week 1 | £2 £2 £2 £ |
    | Week 2 | £2 £2 |
    | Week 3 | £2 £2 £ |
    | Week 4 | £2 £2 £2 £2 |
    | Week 5 | £2 £ |
    | Week 6 | £2 £2 £2 |

    a) How much money did Grace manage to save in Week 1?   _____

    b) How much more did Grace save in Week 4 than Week 5?   _____

    c) In which week did Grace save half as much money as in Week 4?   _____

    d) Grace needs £50 to buy a game. How much more money does she need to save?   _____

Target time: **12 minutes**

1. At half-time in a netball match, 7 players share 35 orange segments between them.

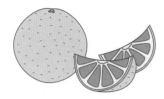

   How many pieces do they each get? _____

2. Mark and his friend Brian go to a football match. It starts at 11:00 a.m. and lasts for $1\frac{1}{2}$ hours. At what time does it finish? _____

3. Alice puts her cake in the oven and sets the timer for 40 minutes. It is due to finish baking at 16:20. At what time did she put it in the oven? _____

4. Write the height of the animals in centimetres.

   340mm   **a)** _____ cm

   730mm   **b)** _____ cm

   1850mm   **c)** _____ cm

5. Identify the type of triangle by measuring its sides.

   a) _____   **b)** _____

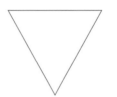   

   c) _____   **d)** _____

   e) _____   **f)** _____

6. Solve these calculations.

   a) 7 × 11 =   _____

   b) 6 × 9 =   _____

   c) 81 ÷ 9 =   _____

   d) _____ ÷ 7 = 6

7. Find these numbers.

   a) What is $\frac{1}{10}$ of 480?   _____

   b) What is $\frac{1}{10}$ of 270?   _____

   c) What is $\frac{1}{100}$ of 5600?   _____

   d) What is $\frac{1}{100}$ of 3500?   _____

Score:		Time taken:		Target met?	

Target time: **12 minutes**

1. Kathryn fills a 5-litre bucket halfway with water. She then adds another 300ml before pouring out 1.4l. How much water is in the bucket now? _____

2. Maisie had £7. She spent £3.50 and then found £1.20 in her bedroom. How much money does she have now? _____

3. Liam bought some football cards with a £10 note. If he got £4.75 change, how much did the cards cost? _____

4. What is 1000 more than 2638? _____

5. What is 1000 less than 6026? _____

6. Round these numbers to the nearest 1000.

    a) 1043 _____

    b) 2789 _____

7. A supermarket sells 364 bottles of orange squash and 287 bottles of lemon squash on Monday, and a further 125 bottles of orange squash on Tuesday. How many bottles of squash does it sell altogether? _____

8. Convert these measurements.

    a) 2.6l = _____ ml

    b) 7100ml = _____ l

    c) 4.6km = _____ m

    d) 2700m = _____ km

    e) 6.3kg = _____ g

    f) 3800g = _____ kg

9. Franny swam for 12 minutes. How many seconds did she swim for? _____

10. There are 245 seats in the cinema. 136 adults and 57 children watched the film. How many seats were empty? _____

11. Rian surveyed children at her school to find out how much television they were allowed to watch each day. The bar chart below shows her results.

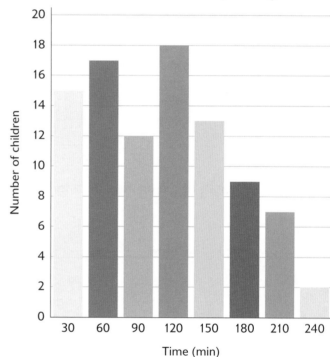

Television time per day

Number of children / Time (min)

a) What was the most frequent amount of television time allowed in hours? _____

b) How many children were only allowed to watch half an hour of television a day? _____

c) How many children were allowed to watch more than 3 hours of television a day? _____

d) How many children took part in the survey? _____

Score:	Time taken:	Target met?

Schofield & Sims

Target time: **12 minutes**

1. Convert these times from the 12-hour clock to the 24-hour clock.

a)

b)

2. Convert these times from the 24-hour clock to the 12-hour clock.

a)

b)

3. The perimeter of a rectangle is 58m. If the length of one side is 17m, what is the width? _____

4. Use this cm² paper to draw a rectangle with a perimeter of 12cm.

5. Complete the table.

Millilitres (ml)	Litres (l) and millilitres (ml)	Fraction (l)	Decimal (l)
100ml	0l 100ml	$\frac{1}{10}$l	0.1l
600ml		$\frac{6}{10}$l	
	1l 200ml		1.2l
1700ml		$1\frac{7}{10}$l	

6. Write these fractions as decimals.

a) $\frac{6}{10}$ _____

b) $\frac{3}{10}$ _____

c) $\frac{3}{100}$ _____

d) $\frac{1}{4}$ _____

7. Karl's football sticker book has space for 379 stickers. He has already stuck in 193 stickers and has got 104 waiting to be stuck in. How many more stickers does he need to collect? _____

8. There were 72 pears on a tree. Gino picked all the pears and shared them between 9 baskets. How many pears were in each basket? _____

9. Draw the lines of symmetry on these shapes.

a) b)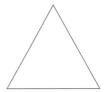

Score:		Time taken:		Target met?	

Maths Rapid Tests 3

Target time: **12 minutes**

1. Write these numbers in words.

    a) 1635

    _____

    _____

    b) 3427

    _____

    _____

2. Write these numbers in digits.

    a) One thousand, six hundred
    and eighty-nine   _____

    b) Two thousand and forty-three _____

3. Complete these sequences.

    a) 225, 250, _____, 300, _____, 350

    b) 7000, _____, 5000, 4000,

    _____, 2000

4. What is the value of the 5 digit in each
    of these numbers?

    a) 4581   _____

    b) 7259   _____

5. Write **<** or **>** to make these statements correct.

    a) 1013 _____ 1130

    b) 1285 _____ 1278

6. Round these numbers to the nearest 100.

    a) 651   _____

    b) 723   _____

7. Round these numbers to the nearest 1000.

    a) 4178   _____

    b) 7450   _____

8. Write the missing numbers on the thermometer

    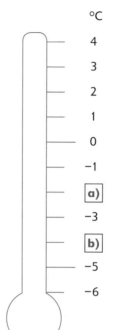

    °C

    a) _____

    b) _____

9. The following number cards were put into a hat.
    Three friends each picked a number.

    Write which number each friend picked.

    a) Mo has an even number
    with 3 hundreds.   _____

    b) Jack has an odd number
    with 3 thousands.   _____

    c) Gabby picks a number
    that is larger than 3800
    but smaller than 5200.   _____

10. Mary thinks of a number that has
    3 digits. It is bigger than 399 but
    smaller than 500. The tens digit is
    smaller than 7 but larger than 5.
    The ones digit is half the tens digit.
    What is her number?   _____

Score:		Time taken:		Target met?	

Target time: **12 minutes**

1. Solve these calculations.

   a)
	3	4
×		7

   b)
	1	9
×		4

   c)
	2	7
×		6

   d)
	9	2
×		3

2. Each train carriage can seat 74 passengers. If a train has 8 carriages, how many passengers can it take? _____

3. On Wes's paper round, he delivers papers to 37 houses every day of the week. How many papers does he deliver each week? _____

4. There were 56 pigeons sitting on 8 telephone wires. If there were the same number of pigeons on each wire, how many pigeons were there on one wire? _____

5. A school is taking 72 children to a museum. Each minibus can hold 12 children.

   How many minibuses does the school need? _____

6. Solve these calculations.

   a) 372 + 286 = _____

   b) 639 − 536 = _____

   c) 12 × _____ = 108

   d) 28 ÷ _____ = 7

   e) 84 ÷ _____ = 7

7. Use column addition to solve these calculations.

   a) 474 + 396 =

   b) 384 + 632 =

8. Use column subtraction to solve these calculations.

   a) 614 − 456 =

   b) 814 − 589 =

9. Amani can fit 82 books on each shelf of her bookcase.

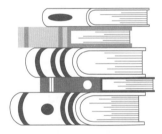

   If her bookcase has 4 shelves, how many books can it hold? _____

10. At this week's football match, there were 473 fans in the north stand and 356 in the south stand. This was an increase of 112 on the previous week. How many fans came to watch last week's match? _____

11. Gethin scored 78 points on level one of 'Strike' and 67 points on level two, but lost 37 points on level three. How many points did he have in total? _____

Score:		Time taken:		Target met?	

Target time: **12 minutes**

1. Find these numbers.

    a) What is $\frac{2}{3}$ of 12? _____

    b) What is $\frac{3}{4}$ of 16? _____

    c) What is $\frac{2}{5}$ of 10? _____

    d) What is $\frac{5}{6}$ of 30? _____

2. Lucy spent the day making cupcakes.

    She made 36 cupcakes altogether. She kept $\frac{4}{9}$ for her family and took the rest to school. How many did she take to school? _____

3. Freddie has collected 48 football cards. He keeps $\frac{3}{8}$ of them and wants to swap the rest. How many does he want to swap? _____

4. Jay counted 108 apples on his apple tree. He picked $\frac{5}{9}$ of them. How many did he leave on the tree?  _____

5. Find these numbers.

    a) What is $\frac{3}{10}$ of 50? _____

    b) What is $\frac{4}{10}$ of 140? _____

    c) What is $\frac{2}{100}$ of 2400? _____

    d) What is $\frac{4}{100}$ of 4300? _____

6. Write the missing decimals.

    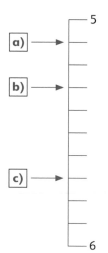

    a) _____

    b) _____

    c) _____

7. Look at these number cards.

    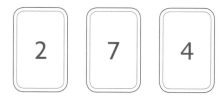

    a) Using these cards, make six 3-digit numbers to one decimal place.

    _____ _____ _____

    _____ _____ _____

    b) Write them in ascending order.

    _____ _____ _____

    _____ _____ _____

8. William's cat weighed 4.6kg. Sohnam's cat weighed 1.3kg more. How much did Sohnam's cat weigh? _____

9. Write these fractions as decimals.

    a) $\frac{1}{4}$ _____

    b) $\frac{1}{2}$ _____

    c) $\frac{3}{4}$ _____

Score: _____   **Time taken:** _____   **Target met?** _____

Target time: **12 minutes**

1. If the following shapes were drawn on cm² paper, what would their areas be?

a)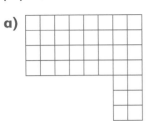

b)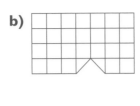

_____ cm²   _____ cm²

2. How many minutes are there in $4\frac{1}{2}$ hours?   _____

3. How many years are there in a decade?   _____

4. Convert these times from the 24-hour clock to the 12-hour digital clock.

a)

b)

5. Draw the hands on the clocks so they show the correct time.

a)

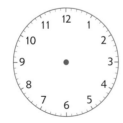

b)

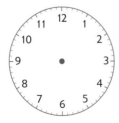

6. Jamie walks 1250m to school. How many kilometres is this?   _____

7. Ed threw a football 1200cm. How many metres is this?   _____

8. Crisps cost £1.60 per packet. How much change did Oli get from £5 if he bought 3 packets?   _____

9. Khalid gets £3.40 pocket money a week. How much does he have after 4 weeks?   _____

10. Convert these measurements.

a) 10.75l = _____ ml

b) 4700ml = _____ l

11. Mira made the following cakes for her friend's birthday.

A   2.4kg   B   3.1kg   C   1.8kg

D   3.7kg   E   2.6kg   F   2.9kg

Each cake needs to be cut into 10 slices. How much will each slice weigh in grams?

Cake	Slice weight (g)
A	
B	
C	
D	
E	
F	

Score:		Time taken:		Target met?	

Target time: **12 minutes**

1. Reflect the shape in the mirror line.

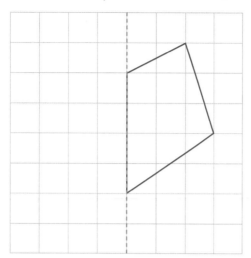

2. a) Plot these coordinates and join them.

(1, 2)   (4, 2)   (5, 4)   (0, 4)

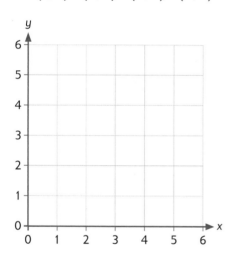

b) Name the shape you have plotted.

_____

3. Shade the acute angles.

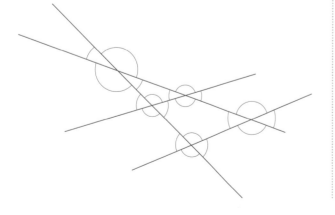

4. Shade the trapeziums.

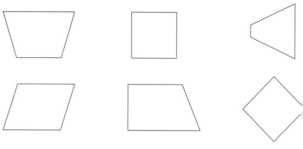

5. Translate this shape 2 squares to the right.

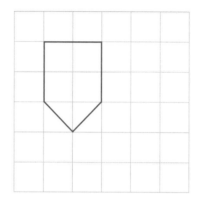

6. a) Plot each pair of coordinates to make two straight lines.

(3, 1) and (7, 5)   (7, 1) and (1, 7)

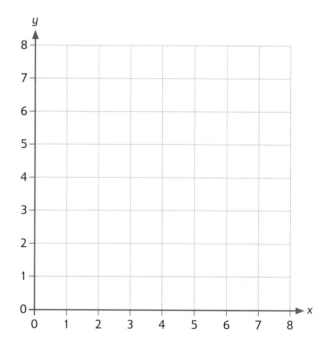

b) Write the coordinates for where the two lines intersect.

(_____, _____)

Score: _____   Time taken: _____   Target met? _____

Maths Rapid Tests 3 Answers

Notes for parents, tutors, teachers and other adult helpers

- **Maths Rapid Tests 3** is designed for eight- and nine-year-olds, but may also be suitable for some children of other ages.

- Remove this pull-out section before giving the book to the child.

- Before the child begins work on the first test, together read the instructions headed **What to do** on page 2. As you do so, point out to the child the suggested **Target time** for completing the test.

- Make sure the child has all the equipment in the list headed **What you need** on page 2. Also ensure that they are able to see a clock or a watch.

- There are three sections in this book. Each section consists of 12 tests. The first six tests focus on specific subject areas and the second six tests are a mix of these subject areas. Each mixed test will include questions from at least three of the subject areas. Details of the subject areas are given in the **Contents** page on page 3.

- Explain to the child how he or she should go about timing the test. Alternatively, you may wish to time the test yourself. When the child has finished the test, together work out the **Time taken** and complete the box that appears at the end of the test.

- Mark the child's work using this pull-out section. Each test is out of 20 marks and each individual question is worth one mark – this means that if a question is split into parts, each part will be worth one mark unless otherwise stated in the answers. If the unit of measure (for example, mm, cm, m, km, g and kg) is not present on the answer line, it should be included as part of the answer to qualify for the mark. Then complete the **Score** box at the end of the test.

- This table shows you how to mark the **Target met?** box and the **Action** notes help you to plan the next step. However, these are suggestions only. Please use your own judgement as you decide how best to proceed.

Score	Time taken	Target met?	Action
1–9	Any	Not yet	Give the child the previous book in the series. Provide help and support as needed.
10–13	Any	Not yet	Encourage the child to keep practising using the tests in this book. The child may need to repeat some tests. If so, wait a few weeks or the child may simply remember the correct answers. Provide help and support as needed.
14–20	Over target – child took too long	Not yet	
14–20	On target – child took suggested time or less	Yes	Encourage the child to keep practising using further tests in this book, and to move on to the next book when you think this is appropriate.

- After finishing each test, the child should fill in the **Progress chart** on page 40.

- Whatever the test score, always encourage the child to have another go at the questions that he or she got wrong – without looking at the answers. If the child's answers are still incorrect, work through these questions together. Demonstrate the correct method if necessary.

- If the child struggles with particular question types or mathematical areas, help him or her to develop the skills and strategies needed.

Answers

Section 1 Test 1 (page 4)

1. a) 54, 60 (+ 6)
    b) 35, 42 (+ 7)
2. a) 700
    b) 40
3. 1567 (567 + 1000)
4. 3285 (4285 − 1000)
5. a) <
    b) >
6. 1320   1302   1203   321   123
7. 6091   6109   6901   9016   9610
8. a) 50 (when the ones are 5 or more, the number is rounded up to the next 10)
    b) 90 (when the ones are 4 or less, the number is rounded down to the existing 10)
9. a) 100 (when the tens are 5 or more, the number is rounded up to the next 100)
    b) 200 (when the tens are 4 or less, the number is rounded down to the existing 100)
10. 3248
11. 7925
12. a) 22
    b) 36
13. a) 125 to 175 (accept any number between 125 and 175)
    b) 775 to 825 (accept any number between 775 and 825)

Section 1 Test 2 (page 5)

1. a)

	2	6	4
+	1	3	2
	3	9	6

   b) 797

2. a)

	4	8	7
−	2	3	5
	2	5	2

   b) 173

3. 52 (97 − 28 = 69, 69 − 17 = 52)
4. 292 (Tilly has 123 + 46 = 169, 169 + 123 = 292)

5. 37 (137 − 52 boys = 85, 85 − 48 girls = 37)
6. 159 (196 − 37 = 159)
7. 253 (376 − 57 = 319, 319 − 66 = 253)
8. a) 56
    b) 27
    c) 12
    d) 8
    e) 238
    f) 162
9. 96 (12 × 8)
10. 810 (135 × 6)
11. 248 (31 × 8)
12. 328 (82 × 4)
13. 192 (64 × 3)

Section 1 Test 3 (page 6)

1. a) $\frac{1}{4}$ $\frac{2}{8}$
    b) $\frac{3}{4}$ $\frac{12}{16}$
2. a) 3 (To find an equivalent fraction, the numerator [top number] and denominator [bottom number] must be multiplied or divided by the same number. Here, both denominators are given but the numerator is missing in the second fraction. To find the missing number, do to the numerators what has been done to the denominators. So 2 × 3 = 6, 1 × 3 = 3.)
    b) 5 (2 has been multiplied by 5 to get 10 so 1 × 5 = 5)
3. a) 6 (24 ÷ 4)
    b) 6 (18 ÷ 3)
    c) 36 (360 ÷ 10)
    d) 23 (2300 ÷ 100)
4. a) $\frac{7}{10}$
    b) $\frac{6}{9}$
    c) $\frac{3}{7}$
    d) $\frac{3}{8}$
5. 16 hr (24 ÷ 3 = 8 so he spent 8 hr sleeping. 24 − 8 = 16 so he spent 16 hr awake.)
6. £2 (50p × 4 = 200p = £2)

A2

Schofield & Sims

7. **a)** 0.1

b) 0.4

8. **a)** 4 (when the tenths are 5 or more, the number is rounded up to the next whole number)

b) 5 (when the tenths are 5 or more, the number is rounded up to the next whole number)

9. 1.25l or $1\frac{1}{4}$l (0.25l × 5)

10. 0.5kg or $\frac{1}{2}$kg (6 × 0.3kg = 1.8kg, 2.3kg − 1.8kg = 0.5kg)

Section 1 Test 4 (page 7)

1. (1 mark for each correct answer. Max. 4 marks.)

Grams (g)	Kilograms (kg) and grams (g)	Fraction (kg)	Decimal (kg)
500g	0kg 500g	$\frac{1}{2}$kg	0.5kg
800g	0kg 800g	$\frac{8}{10}$kg	0.8kg
1200g	1kg 200g	$1\frac{2}{10}$kg	1.2kg

2. **a)** 7:20

b) 1:55

3. 103 (8 × 12 = 96 months, 96 + 7 = 103 months)

4. **a)** 43.8cm (remember there are 10mm in 1cm)

b) 21.3cm

c) 38.7cm

5. **a)** 25cm (5cm + 5cm + 5cm + 5cm + 5cm)

b) 18cm (7cm + 7cm + 4cm)

c) 34cm (12cm + 12cm + 5cm + 5cm)

6. **a)** 65p (30p + 15p + 20p)

b) £1.35 (£2 − 65p)

7. **a)** £1.20 (35p + 35p + 50p)

b) 20p (£1.20 − £1)

8. **a)** 70ml

b) 45ml

c) 25ml (70ml − 45ml)

Section 1 Test 5 (page 8)

1. **a)** 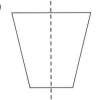 **b)**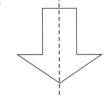

c) 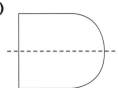 **d)**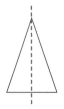

2. (1 mark for a correctly drawn reflection)

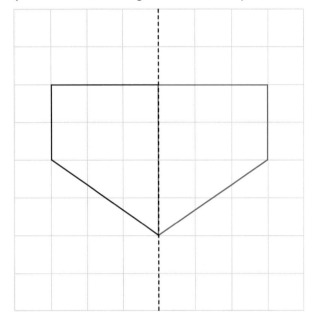

3. **a)** acute (less than 90°)

b) obtuse (more than 90° but less than 180°)

c) obtuse (more than 90° but less than 180°)

4. (1 mark for each correct answer. Max. 6 marks.)

Quadrilateral	Number of pairs of parallel sides
Square	2
Rectangle	2
Trapezium	1
Kite	0
Rhombus	2
Parallelogram	2

5. **a)** G7

b) E3

c) A4

d) H2

e) D6

f) C1

Answers

Section 1 Test 6 (page 9)

1. **a)** (1 mark for each correct section. Max. 10 marks.)

Team	Tally	Total
Longhorn	|||||		6
Gamble	|||||		6
Claremont	||||| ||	7
Stratton	|||||		6
St. John's	||||| ||	7

b) (1 mark for each correct bar. Max. 5 marks.)

Autumn term football

2. **a)** 10:00
   b) 15:00
   c) 17:00
   d) 3 hr
   e) 15:00 (this is where the line starts to drop)

Section 1 Test 7 (page 10)

1. 36 (112 + 87 = 199, 235 − 199 = 36)
2. 270 (500 − 96 = 404, 404 − 134 = 270)
3. 6246   4632   4263   3462   2634
4. **a)** nine hundred and forty-eight
   b) one thousand and four
5. 12 (144 ÷ 12)
6. 8 (32 ÷ 4)

7. **a)** 4 (20 ÷ 5)
   b) 9 (36 ÷ 4)
   c) 7 (42 ÷ 6)
8. 27 (30 ÷ 10 = 3, 30 − 3 = 27)
9. **a)** 1:19 a.m.
   b) 4:32 a.m.
10. 2 p.m.
11. **a)** 1400ml (remember there are 1000ml in 1l)
   b) 1.6km (remember there are 1000m in 1km)
   c) 5.2l
   d) 1300m
12. **a)** 62cm (22cm + 22cm + 9cm + 9cm)
   b) 52cm (12cm + 12cm + 14cm + 14cm)

Section 1 Test 8 (page 11)

1. 58m (18m + 18m + 11m + 11m)
2. 9cm (36cm ÷ 4)
3. 36cm (there are 10mm in 1cm so 360mm ÷ 10 = 36cm)
4. 5kg (33kg − 28kg)
5. **a)** 532
   b) 349
6. **a)** trapezium
   b) kite
   c) rhombus
   d) parallelogram
7. **a)** 6 (2 has been multiplied by 6 to get 12 so 1 × 6 = 6)
   b) 8 (2 has been multiplied by 8 to get 16 so 1 × 8 = 8)
   c) 2 (4 has been multiplied by 2 to get 8 so 1 × 2 = 2)
   d) 6 (4 has been multiplied by 6 to get 24 so 1 × 6 = 6)
8. 171 (245 + 213 = 458 books on top and bottom shelf. 629 − 458 = 171.)
9. **a)** £2.35 (60p + 60p + 25p + 90p)
   b) 50p (60p + 75p + 15p = £1.50, £2 − £1.50 = 50p)
   c) £2.10 (25p + 25p + 25p + 15p = 90p, £3 − 90p = £2.10)
   d) 25p (90p + 75p + 60p = £2.25. Emma only had £2 so, £2.25 − £2 = 25p more needed.)
   e) scissors and pen (90p + 60p = £1.50)

Section 1 Test 9 (page 12)

1. $\frac{2}{4}$ $\frac{8}{16}$

2. **a)** 3 (3 has been multiplied by 3 to get 9
   so 1 × 3 = 3)

   b) 2 (5 has been multiplied by 2 to get 10
   so 1 x 2 = 2)

   c) 4 (6 has been multiplied by 4 to get 24
   so 1 x 4 = 4)

3. **a)** 63, 72 (+ 9)

   b) 21, 35 (+ 7)

4. **a)** 639

   b) 1274

5. 6.1m (4.8m + 1.3m)

6. 2.7l (4.6l − 1.9l)

7. **a)** and **b)** two of the following factor pairs:
   1 and 12, 2 and 6, or 3 and 4 (a) and b) can be
   either way round)

8. **a)** 4700g (remember there are 1000g in 1kg)

   b) 1.6kg

9. **a)**    **b)**

10. **a)** £7 (remember that each coin image is worth £2)

    b) £5

    c) 2

    d) £17

Section 1 Test 10 (page 13)

1. 5 (35 ÷ 7)

2. 12:30 p.m.

3. 15:40 (16:20 − 40 min)

4. **a)** 34cm (remember there are 10mm in 1cm)

   b) 73cm

   c) 185cm

5. **a)** equilateral (all sides the same length)

   b) isosceles (2 sides the same length)

   c) equilateral (all sides the same length)

   d) scalene (no sides the same length)

   e) isosceles (2 sides the same length)

   f) scalene (no sides the same length)

6. **a)** 77

   b) 54

   c) 9

   d) 42

7. **a)** 48 (480 ÷ 10)

   b) 27 (270 ÷ 10)

   c) 56 (5600 ÷ 100)

   d) 35 (3500 ÷ 100)

Section 1 Test 11 (page 14)

1. 1.4l or 1400ml (5l ÷ 2 = 2500ml, 2500ml + 300ml
   = 2800ml, 2800ml − 1400ml = 1400ml)

2. £4.70 (£7 − £3.50 = £3.50, £3.50 + £1.20 = £4.70)

3. £5.25 (£10 − £4.75)

4. 3638 (2638 + 1000)

5. 5026 (6026 − 1000)

6. **a)** 1000 (when the hundreds are 4 or less, the
   number is rounded down to the existing 1000)

   b) 3000 (when the hundreds are 5 or more, the
   number is rounded up to the next 1000)

7. 776 (364 + 287 + 125)

8. **a)** 2600ml

   b) 7.1l

   c) 4600m

   d) 2.7km

   e) 6300g

   f) 3.8kg

9. 720 sec (12 × 60 sec)

10. 52 (136 + 57 = 193, 245 − 193 = 52)

11. **a)** 2 hr

    b) 15

    c) 9 (more than 3 hr means more than 180 min,
    not 180 min)

    d) 93

Section 1 Test 12 (page 15)

1. **a)** 07:14

   b) 13:27

2. **a)** 3:53 p.m.

   b) 3:45 a.m.

Answers

Section 1 Test 12 (page 15) continued

3. 12m (The 2 lengths together = 34m. 58m − 34m = 24m so the 2 widths = 24m. 24m ÷ 2 = 12m.)

4. (either 4cm × 2cm or 5cm × 1cm)

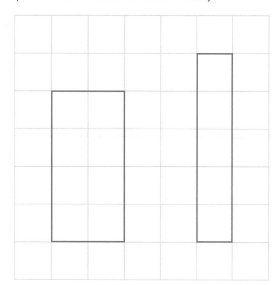

5. (1 mark for each correct answer. Max. 6 marks.)

Millilitres (ml)	Litres (l) and millilitres (ml)	Fraction (l)	Decimal (l)
100ml	0l 100ml	$\frac{1}{10}$l	0.1l
600ml	0l 600ml	$\frac{6}{10}$l	0.6l
1200ml	1l 200ml	$1\frac{2}{10}$l	1.2l
1700ml	1l 700ml	$1\frac{7}{10}$l	1.7l

6. **a)** 0.6 (the first digit after a decimal point is worth $\frac{1}{10}$)

   b) 0.3

   c) 0.03

   d) 0.25

7. 82 (379 − 193 = 186, 186 − 104 = 82)

8. 8 (72 ÷ 9)

9. (all lines correct for 1 mark)

a) 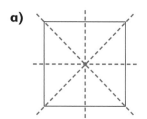   **b)**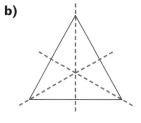

Section 2 Test 1 (page 16)

1. **a)** one thousand, six hundred and thirty-five

   b) three thousand, four hundred and twenty-seven

2. **a)** 1689

   b) 2043

3. **a)** 275, 325 (+ 25)

   b) 6000, 3000 (− 1000)

4. **a)** 500

   b) 50

5. **a)** <

   b) >

6. **a)** 700 (when the tens are 5 or more, the number is rounded up to the next 100)

   b) 700 (when the tens are 4 or less, the number is rounded down to the existing 100)

7. **a)** 4000 (when the hundreds are 4 or less, the number is rounded down to the existing 1000)

   b) 7000 (when the hundreds are 4 or less, the number is rounded down to the existing 1000)

8. **a)** −2

   b) −4

9. **a)** 5364

   b) 3465

   c) 4365

10. 463

Section 2 Test 2 (page 17)

1. **a)** 238

   b) 76

   c) 162

   d) 276

2. 592 (74 × 8)

3. 259 (37 × 7)

4. 7 (56 ÷ 8)

5. 6 (72 ÷ 12)

6. **a)** 658

   b) 103

   c) 9

   d) 4

   e) 12

7. **a)** 870

   b) 1016

8. a)

	$^5\cancel{6}$	$^{10}\cancel{7}$	^{14}
−	4	5	6
	1	5	8

b)

	$^7\cancel{8}$	$^{10}\cancel{7}$	^{14}
−	5	8	9
	2	2	5

9. 328 (82 × 4)

10. 717 (473 + 356 = 829, 829 − 112 = 717)

11. 108 (78 + 67 = 145, 145 − 37 = 108)

Section 2 Test 3 (page 18)

1. a) 8 (12 ÷ 3 = 4, 4 × 2 = 8)

b) 12 (16 ÷ 4 = 4, 4 × 3 = 12)

c) 4 (10 ÷ 5 = 2, 2 × 2 = 4)

d) 25 (30 ÷ 6 = 5, 5 × 5 = 25)

2. 20 (She kept $\frac{4}{9}$ so she took $\frac{5}{9}$ into school. 36 ÷ 9 = 4, 4 × 5 = 20.)

3. 30 (He keeps $\frac{3}{8}$ so wants to swap $\frac{5}{8}$. 48 ÷ 8 = 6, 6 × 5 = 30.)

4. 48 (He picked $\frac{5}{9}$ so left $\frac{4}{9}$ on the tree. 108 ÷ 9 = 12, 12 × 4 = 48.)

5. a) 15 (50 ÷ 10 = 5, 5 × 3 = 15)

b) 56 (140 ÷ 10 = 14, 14 × 4 = 56)

c) 48 (2400 ÷ 100 = 24, 24 × 2 = 48)

d) 172 (4300 ÷ 100 = 43, 43 × 4 = 172)

6. a) 5.1 (there are 10 divisions between 5 and 6 so each division is worth 0.1)

b) 5.3

c) 5.7

7. a) 27.4 24.7 72.4 74.2 47.2 42.7 (can be in any order)

b) 24.7 27.4 42.7 47.2 72.4 74.2 (the easiest way to order decimals is to imagine the decimal point is no longer there so instead you have whole numbers to order, e.g. 274, 247, 724, 742, 472, 427)

8. 5.9kg (4.6kg + 1.3kg)

9. a) 0.25

b) 0.5

c) 0.75

Section 2 Test 4 (page 19)

1. a) 38cm² (count the number of squares)

b) 27cm² (Count the number of squares. If a square is cut exactly in half, the triangle is worth $\frac{1}{2}$cm².)

2. 270 min (60 min in an hr, so 4 × 60 min = 240 min, plus 30 min [$\frac{1}{2}$ an hr] = 270 min)

3. 10

4. a) 12:47 p.m.

b) 7:17 a.m.

5. a)    **b)**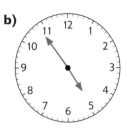

6. 1.25km or $1\frac{1}{4}$km (there are 1000m in 1km)

7. 12m (there are 100cm in 1m)

8. 20p (£1.60 × 3 = £4.80, £5 − £4.80 = 20p)

9. £13.60 (£3.40 × 4)

10. a) 10750ml (there are 1000ml in 1l)

b) 4.7l

11. (1 mark for each correct answer. Max. 6 marks. To work out the weight of a slice, first convert the weight of the whole cake into grams. Then divide that by 10, e.g. Cake A = 2.4kg = 2400g, 2400g ÷ 10 = 240g.)

Cake	Slice weight (g)
A	240g
B	310g
C	180g
D	370g
E	260g
F	290g

Section 2 Test 5 (page 20)

1. (1 mark for a correctly drawn reflection)

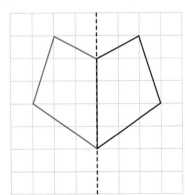

Answers

2. **a)** (1 mark for each correct coordinate. Max. 4 marks.)

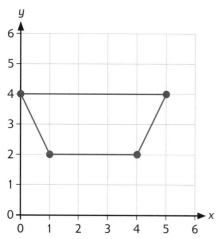

b) trapezium

3. (1 mark for each correct pair of angles. Max. 5 marks. Acute angles are less than 90°.)

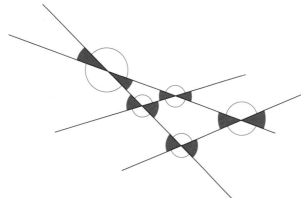

4. (1 mark for each shaded trapezium. Max. 3 marks. A trapezium has 4 sides and 1 pair of parallel sides.)

5. (1 mark for a correct translation. Translating a shape means moving either left or right and up or down.)

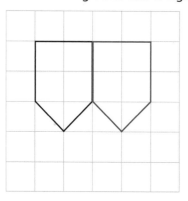

6. **a)** (1 mark for each correct coordinate. Max. 4 marks.)

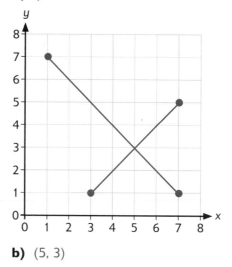

b) (5, 3)

Section 2 Test 6 (page 21)

1. **a)** (1 mark for each correct tally. Max. 6 marks.)

Difference	Tally	Total
0	IIII	4
1	IIII III	8
2	IIII I	6
3	IIII	5
4	IIII	5
5	II	2

b) (1 mark for each correct bar. Max. 6 marks.)

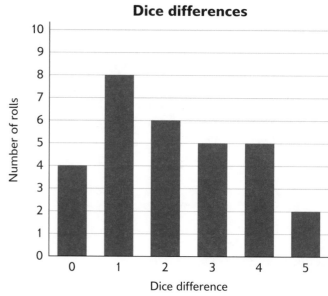

c) 1

2. a) (1 mark for each correct bar. Max. 6 marks. Remember each face is worth 6 votes.)

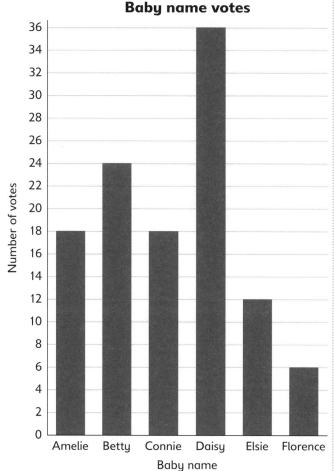

Baby name votes

b) 114

Section 2 Test 7 (page 22)

1. a) 260

b) 612

c) 568

d) 399

2. a) 24cm²

b) 26cm²

3. a) 1.1kg (remember there are 1000g in 1kg)

b) 0.1kg

c) 0.4kg

d) 5.5kg or $5\frac{1}{2}$kg

4. a) 1.2 (12 ÷ 10)

b) 4.5 (45 ÷ 10)

c) 56.8 (5680 ÷ 100)

d) 0.86 (86 ÷ 100)

5. a) £2.05 (85p + 60p + 60p)

b) 40p (35p + 35p + 50p + 40p = £1.60, £2 − £1.60 = 40p)

c) 50p (85p + 85p + 40p + 40p = £2.50, £3 − £2.50 = 50p)

d) £2.80 (35p + 35p + 35p + 35p + 60p + 40p + 40p)

e) £2.30 (50p + 35p + 60p + 85p + 40p = £2.70, £5 − £2.70 = £2.30)

6. 448 (56 × 8)

Section 2 Test 8 (page 23)

1. (1 mark for each correct answer. Max. 6 marks.)

Metres (m)	Fraction (km)	Decimal (km)
1500m	$1\frac{1}{2}$ km	1.5km
2600m	$2\frac{6}{10}$ km	2.6km
3700m	$3\frac{7}{10}$ km	3.7km
4300m	$4\frac{3}{10}$ km	4.3km

2. 165 min (2 hr = 120 min, $\frac{3}{4}$ hr = 45 min, 120 min + 45 min = 165 min)

3. 1500 sec (25 × 60 sec)

4. 42 (6 × 7)

5. 189 (27 × 7)

6. a) $\frac{3}{5}$

b) $\frac{11}{12}$

c) $\frac{2}{9}$

d) $\frac{5}{10}$ or $\frac{1}{2}$

7. a)   **b)**

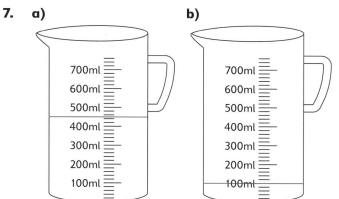

8. a) 3918

b) 5254

9. eight thousand, one hundred and four

10. 672 (894 − 564 = 330, 330 + 342 = 672)

Answers

Section 2 Test 9 (page 24)

1. a) 1256
    b) 537
    c) 1644
    d) 1506
2. 50 (65 × 8 = 520, 520 − 470 = 50)
3. 1002 (238 + 467 + 297)
4. 27 (If she found $\frac{5}{8}$ in the park, she found $\frac{3}{8}$ in the school field. 72 ÷ 8 = 9, 9 × 3 = 27.)
5. 10 (200ml ÷ 20ml)
6. a) 27, 2.7 (1 mark for each correct answer. Max. 2 marks.)
    b) 36, 3.6 (1 mark for each correct answer. Max. 2 marks.)
7. a) 21:03
    b) 16:39
    c) 13:12
    d) 17:34
8. a) acute (less than 90°)
    b) right angle (90°)
    c) obtuse (greater than 90° but less than 180°)
9. 180m (If $\frac{4}{10}$ was uphill then $\frac{6}{10}$ was flat. 300m ÷ 10 = 30m, 30m × 6 = 180m.)

Section 2 Test 10 (page 25)

1. a) (1 mark for each point. Max. 6 marks.)

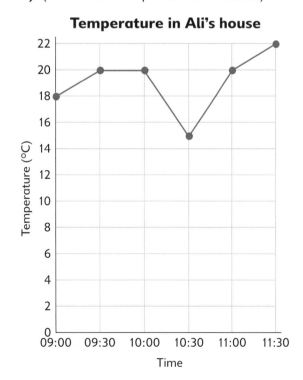

Temperature in Ali's house

    b) 11:30
    c) 19°C
    d) 10:00
2. 500g or $\frac{1}{2}$kg (0.8kg = 800g. 800g + 400g = 1200g, 1.7kg = 1700g. 1700g − 1200g = 500g.)
3. a) 8900ml
    b) 2.75l or $2\frac{3}{4}$l
    c) 1.25km or $1\frac{1}{4}$km
    d) 11 800m
    e) 3600g
    f) 4.25kg or $4\frac{1}{4}$kg
4. 65p (£6.50 ÷ 10)
5. (3, 5)
6. 2:15 p.m. (4:30 − 2 hr = 2:30, 2:30 − 15 min = 2:15)
7. 12 (96 ÷ 8)

Section 2 Test 11 (page 26)

1. a) −8
    b) −5
    c) −4
    d) −1
    e) 0
2. a) 1000 (when the tens are 5 or more, the number is rounded up to the next 100)
    b) 9500 (when the tens are 4 or less, the number is rounded down to the existing 100)
3. 288 (48 × 6)
4. 1.07m (1.34m − 0.27m)
5. 80p (£3.20 ÷ 8 = 40p so one bracelet costs 40p. 40p × 2 = 80p.)
6. 257 (35 × 7 = 245, 245 + 12 = 257)
7. a) 70 (10 has been multiplied by 10 to get 100 so 7 × 10 = 70)
    b) 2 (10 has been divided by 2 to get 5 so 4 ÷ 2 = 2)
    c) 1 (9 has been divided by 3 to get 3 so 3 ÷ 3 = 1)
8. a) 840ml
    b) 0.66l

9. (1 mark for each correct reflection. Max. 3 marks.)

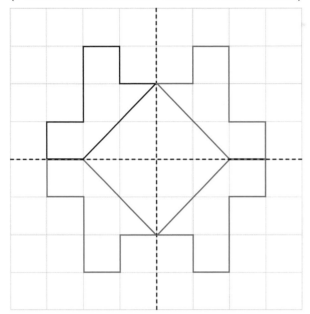

10. 50 (500ml ÷ 10ml)

Section 2 Test 12 (page 27)

1. (must have sides of 4cm)

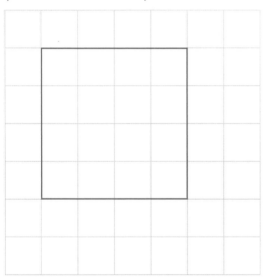

2. a) 2 (when the tenths are 5 or more, the number is rounded up to the next one)

b) 4

c) 3

3. a) 1265

b) 281

c) 605

d) 9

4. 48 (4 × 12)

5. 17 000km (when the tens are 5 or more, the number is rounded up to the next 100)

6. a) 5.9km (Rainham to Redland = 1700m, Redland to Newtown = 4200m. 4200m + 1700m = 5900m = 5.9km.)

b) 2.6km (Marcham to Rainham = 900m, Rainham to Redland = 1700m. 900m + 1700m = 2600m = 2.6km.)

c) 4.9km (Newtown to Lendon = 3800m, Lendon to Marcham = 1100m. 3800m + 1100m = 4900m = 4.9km.)

d) 2km (Rainham to Marcham = 900m, Marcham to Lendon = 1100m. 900m + 1100m = 2000m = 2km.)

7. a) $\frac{7}{10}$

b) $\frac{7}{8}$

c) $\frac{3}{16}$

d) $\frac{1}{9}$

8. $\frac{3}{10}$ $(3 \div 10 = \frac{3}{10})$

9. $\frac{1}{3}$ or $\frac{4}{12}$ $(4 \div 12 = \frac{1}{3})$

Section 3 Test 1 (page 28)

1. a) 7855   7585   5785   5780   5078

b) 21   14   8   2   −7   −12   −18

2. a) 3174   3417   3471   3714   3741

b) −24   −10   −2   0   4   5   15

3. a) 372 (C = 100, L = 50, X = 10, I = 1)

b) 1238 (M = 1000)

4. a) 17 000, 18 000 (+ 1000)

b) 38 000, 40 000 (+ 1000)

c) 4200, 3900 (− 100)

5. a) 900

b) 9000

6. 311

7. a) <

b) >

8. a) 1000 (when the tens are 5 or more, the number is rounded up to the next 100)

b) 1000 (when the hundreds are 5 or more, the number is rounded up to the next 1000)

c) 9500 (when the tens are 4 or less, the number is rounded down to the existing 100)

d) 10 000 (when the hundreds are 5 or more, the number is rounded up to the next 1000)

9. 25, 30, 75 (all multiples of 5 end in 0 or 5)

10. 8764

Answers

Section 3 Test 2 (page 29)

1. a) −2
    b) −4
    c) 1104
    d) 290

2. 738 (246 × 2 = 492 homes on the other side of the street. 492 + 246 = 738 homes in total.)

3. 210 (527 − 317 = 210)

4. a) 21
    b) 17
    c) 8

5. a) 1256
    b) 537
    c) 1644
    d) 1506
    e) 11
    f) 48
    g) 72
    h) 12

6. 744 (124 × 6)

7. a) 1 and 51 } (can be either
    b) 3 and 17 } way round)

Section 3 Test 3 (page 30)

1. a) 9 (12 ÷ 4 = 3, 3 × 3 = 9)
    b) 12 (40 ÷ 10 = 4, 4 × 3 = 12)
    c) 15 (24 ÷ 8 = 3, 3 × 5 = 15)
    d) 24 (40 ÷ 5 = 8, 8 × 3 = 24)

2. a) 1 (12 has been divided by 4 to get 3 so 4 ÷ 4 = 1)
    b) 2 (15 has been divided by 3 to get 5 so 6 ÷ 3 = 2)

3. 63 ($\frac{2}{11}$ were lambs so $\frac{9}{11}$ were adult sheep. 77 ÷ 11 = 7, 7 × 9 = 63.)

4. 24 ($\frac{2}{6}$ were red admirals so $\frac{4}{6}$ were cabbage whites. 36 ÷ 6 = 6, 6 × 4 = 24.)

5. a) $5\frac{1}{5}$ (there are five divisions between each whole number so each division is worth $\frac{1}{5}$)
    b) $6\frac{2}{5}$

6. a) 8.2 (there are five divisions between each whole number so each division is worth 0.2)
    b) 8.8

7. a) 3.69   3.96   6.39   6.93   9.63   9.36 (can be in any order)
    b) 3.69   3.96   6.39   6.93   9.36   9.63 (the easiest way to order decimals is to imagine the decimal point is not there so instead you have whole numbers to order, e.g. 369, 396, 639, 693, 963, 936)

8. 4.9m

9. a) 0.7, 0.8 (+ 0.1)
    b) 1.26, 1.27 (+ 0.01)

10. 13.7 sec (Remember that a slower time is a higher number of seconds. 12.4 sec + 1.3 sec = 13.7 sec.)

11. £4.50 (If she saved $\frac{3}{4}$ of her money, then she spent $\frac{1}{4}$. If $\frac{1}{4}$ of the money is £1.50, then $\frac{3}{4}$ is £1.50 × 3 = £4.50.)

12. 17.4 km (8.7km + 8.7km)

Section 3 Test 4 (page 31)

1. 18cm² (Count each square. If a square has been cut exactly in half it is worth $\frac{1}{2}$cm².)

2. 366

3. 14

4. 300 sec (5 × 60)

5. a) 05:46
    b) 10:26

6. £20.50 (£48 − £27.50)

7. 25 (5 × 20p coins = £1 so 25 × 20p = £5)

8. 15 (10p × 15 = £1.50)

9. 29p ($\frac{1}{2}$kg of apples = 19p, 1kg of oranges cost 52p. In total, 19p + 52p = 71p. £1 − 71p = 29p.)

10. 700g or 0.7kg (800g + 600g + 1200g + 200g = 2800g. 3500g − 2800g = 700g.)

11. a) 0.25l (remember there are 1000ml in 1l)
    b) 0.5l
    c) 0.33l
    d) 0.15l
    e) 0.85l
    f) lemonade and milk
    g) apple juice and cola
    h) water and milk
    i) lemonade and water

Answers

Section 3 Test 5 (page 32)

1. (1 mark for each correctly drawn reflection. Max. 3 marks.)

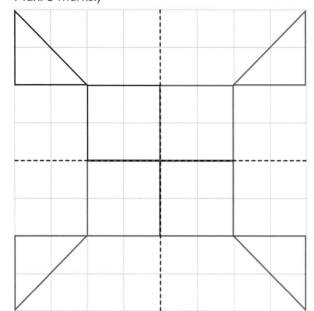

2. (1 mark for a correct translation)

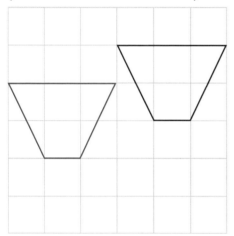

3. (acute angles are less than 90°)

a) 3 **b)** 2 **c)** 2

4. (obtuse angles are greater than 90° and less than 180°)

a) 3 **b)** 0 **c)** 2

5. a) (1 mark for each correct coordinate. Max. 4 marks.)

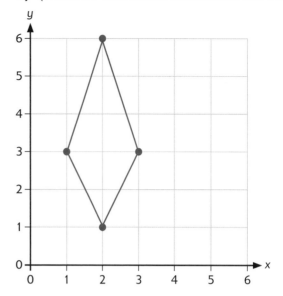

b) kite

6. square-based pyramid

7. cylinder

8. a) **b)** **c)**

Section 3 Test 6 (page 33)

1. a) (1 mark for each correct answer. Max. 6 marks.)

Flavour	Tally	Total
Vanilla	JHT JHT JHT JHT JHT II	27
Chocolate	JHT JHT JHT JHT II	22
Strawberry	JHT JHT JHT III	18
Coconut	JHT II	7
Pistachio	JHT JHT	10
Mint	JHT JHT I	11

Answers

Section 3 Test 6 (page 33) continued

b) (1 mark for each correct bar. Max. 6 marks.)

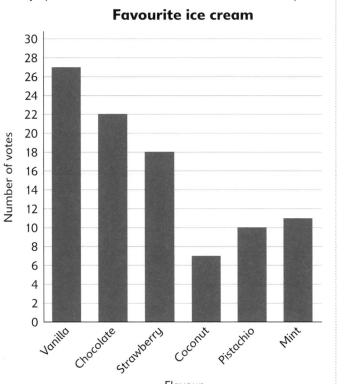

Favourite ice cream

c) 11

d) chocolate

e) strawberry

f) 95

2. **a)** Thursday

b) 5°C

c) Saturday and Sunday

d) 3

Section 3 Test 7 (page 34)

1. **a)** (3, 6)

b) (6, 4)

c) (5, 1)

d) (2, 0)

e) (1, 3)

2. 1.05l (1300ml − 250ml = 1050ml = 1.05l)

3. **a)** 7 (£2 = 200p. 200 ÷ 26 = 7 r.18, so I could buy 7 packets.)

b) 18p (7 × 26p = 182p, so £2 − 182p = 18p change)

4. 720ml (0.28l = 280ml. 1000ml − 280ml = 720ml.)

5. 2700g or 2.7kg (200g + 200g + 300g + 300g + 300g + 1400g = 2700g)

6. **a)** 7609

b) 9006

7. **a)** <

b) >

c) >

8. 12:20 p.m.

9. **a)** 6000 (when the hundreds are 5 or more, the number is rounded up to the next 1000)

b) 4000 (when the hundreds are 5 or more, the number is rounded up to the next 1000)

c) 1000 (when the hundreds are 4 or less, the number is rounded down to the existing 1000)

10. 27 (36 ÷ 4 = 9, 9 × 3 = 27)

Section 3 Test 8 (page 35)

1. 1.61l (230ml + 460ml + 920ml = 1610ml = 1.61l)

2. (1 mark for each correct answer. Max. 7 marks.)

Millilitres (ml)	Litres (l) and millilitres (ml)	Decimal (l)	Fraction (l)
400ml	0l 400ml	0.4l	$\frac{4}{10}$l
1200ml	1l 200ml	1.2l	$1\frac{2}{10}$l
2700ml	2l 700ml	2.7l	$2\frac{7}{10}$l
3600ml	3l 600ml	3.6l	$3\frac{6}{10}$l

3. 450g (1300g − 200g = 1100g, 1100g − 400g = 700g, 700g − 250g = 450g)

4. **a)** 19:42

b) 04:38

5. 75 min

6. 6cm (An equilateral triangle has 3 equal sides. 18cm ÷ 3 = 6cm.)

7. 18 (If $\frac{2}{5}$ were milk chocolate and $\frac{1}{5}$ were dark then $\frac{2}{5}$ were white. 45 ÷ 5 = 9, 9 × 2 = 18.)

8. **a)** $\frac{9}{12}$ or $\frac{3}{4}$

b) $\frac{2}{4}$ or $\frac{1}{2}$

c) $\frac{4}{13}$

9. 7 (108 ÷ 12 = 9, 9 − 2 = 7)

10. **a)** LXII (XXI = 21, XLI = 41, 21 + 41 = 62 = LXII)

b) CXVI (XC = 90, XXVI = 26, 90 + 26 = 116 = CXVI)

Section 3 Test 9 (page 36)

1. **a)** (1 mark for each correct answer. Max. 8 marks. There are 10 divisions between each whole kg so each division is worth 0.1kg.)

Child	Guessed mass (kg)	Nearest kilogram
Martha	3.7kg	4kg
Denny	3.4kg	3kg
Simon	3.1kg	3kg
Sara	2.9kg	3kg

   b) Simon

2. 4 (28 ÷ 7)

3. **a)** 2472

   b) 2814

   c) 1166

   d) 1291

   e) 187

   f) 218

4. 8 (48 ÷ 6)

5. 20p (If she spent $\frac{3}{4}$ of her money, she saved $\frac{1}{4}$. 80p ÷ 4 = 20p.)

6. 6.21 6.12 2.61 1.62 1.26 (the easiest way to order decimals is to imagine the decimal point is not there so instead you have whole numbers to order, e.g. 162, 126, 261, 612, 621)

7. 1.55 5.05 5.15 5.5 5.51 (To order easily, all decimals need the same number of digits after the decimal point. 5.5 only has 1 digit after the decimal while all the others have 2 digits so you need to put a zero on the end, e.g. 5.50. This does not change the value of the number. Now imagine the decimals are 3-digit whole numbers, e.g. 551, 155, 515, 505, 550. Now put them in order.)

Section 3 Test 10 (page 37)

1. **a)** 51, 5.1 (1 mark for each correct answer. Max. 2 marks.)

   b) 750, 75 (1 mark for each correct answer. Max. 2 marks.)

2. 0.7m (1.2m − 0.5m)

3. 47.2 seconds (24.7 sec + 22.5 sec)

4. 17cm² (Count all the whole squares. Then count any squares that are more than $\frac{1}{2}$ a square and count them as a whole square. Ignore any squares that are less than $\frac{1}{2}$ a square.)

5. 440m (when the ones are 4 or less, the number is rounded down to the existing 10)

6. 2400cm (There are 100cm in 1m. 24 × 100cm = 2400cm.)

7. **a)** £4.79

   b) £6.89

   c) £2.13

   d) £3.32

8. 1.75l or $1\frac{3}{4}$l (250ml × 7 = 1750ml = 1.7l)

9. **a)** nine thousand and eighty-six

   b) thirteen thousand, nine hundred and six

10. $\frac{5}{8}$ (5 ÷ 8 = $\frac{5}{8}$)

11. **a)** >

    b) >

    c) <

Section 3 Test 11 (page 38)

1. **a)** 39.6kg

   b) 37.8kg

   c) 1.8kg (39.6kg − 37.8kg)

2. 4.1l (200ml × 8 = 1600ml, 500ml × 5 = 2500ml, 1600ml + 2500ml = 4100ml = 4.1l)

3. 525ml (half a carton is 350ml ÷ 2 = 175ml, 350ml + 175ml = 525ml)

4. 700g or 0.7kg (1.8kg ÷ 2 = 0.9kg so Ava took 0.9kg leaving 0.9kg = 900g. If there were only 200g left after Adam took some biscuits, 900g − 200g = 700g, so Adam must have taken 700g.)

5. **a)** 259

   b) 7394

   c) 4914

Answers

Section 3 Test 11 (page 38) continued

6. **a)** (1 mark for each correct coordinate. Max. 4 marks.)

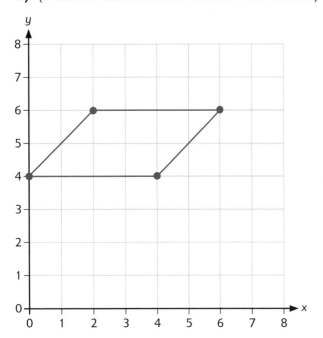

b) parallelogram

7. **a)** 12.75 or $12\frac{3}{4}$ kg

b) 10.5m or $10\frac{1}{2}$ m

c) 11.2km

d) 4.25l or $4\frac{1}{4}$ l

8. 400m (If she swam $\frac{2}{10}$ breaststroke and $\frac{3}{10}$ backstroke, that totals $\frac{5}{10}$, leaving $\frac{5}{10}$ that she swam front crawl. 800m ÷ 10 = 80m, 80m × 5 = 400m.)

9. 36 (144 ÷ 12 = 12, 12 × 3 = 36)

Section 3 Test 12 (page 39)

1. **a)** XLVII

b) LXXI

c) CXXIX

d) CDLVI

2. **a)** (1 mark for each correct point. Max. 7 marks.)

Cross section of hill

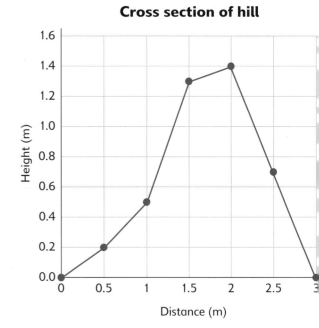

b) 0.1m

c) 1m and 1.5m

3. 13cm (55mm + 75mm = 130mm. 10mm = 1cm so 130mm ÷ 10 = 13cm.)

4. 8 min (240 sec × 2 = 480 sec to cycle twice round the garden. 480 sec ÷ 60 = 8 min.)

5. 3:20 p.m. (11:40 + 3 hr = 2:40 p.m., 2:40 p.m. + 40 min = 3:20 p.m.)

6. 800g (0.3kg + 0.5kg = 0.8kg = 800g)

7. £17.75 (£12 + £4.50 + £1.25)

8. **a)** 2.6 (There are 10 divisions between 2 and 4. That means there would be 5 divisions between 2 and 3 so each division would be worth 0.2.)

b) 3.8

This book of answers is a pull-out section from **Maths Rapid Tests 3**.

Published by **Schofield & Sims Ltd**,
7 Mariner Court, Wakefield, West Yorkshire WF4 3FL, UK
Telephone 01484 607080
www.schofieldandsims.co.uk

This edition copyright © Schofield & Sims Ltd, 2018
First published in 2018

Author: **Rebecca Brant**. Rebecca Brant has asserted her moral rights under the Copyright, Designs and Patents Act, 1988, to be identified as the author of this work.

British Library Cataloguing in Publication Data. A catalogue record for this book is available from the British Library.

All rights reserved. No part of this publication may be reproduced, stored in a retrieval system, or transmitted in any form or by any means, electronic, mechanical, photocopying, recording or otherwise, without either the prior permission of the publisher or a licence permitting restricted copying in the United Kingdom issued by the Copyright Licensing Agency Limited, Barnard's Inn, 86 Fetter Lane, London EC4A 1EN.

Design by **Ledgard Jepson Ltd**
Printed in the UK by **Page Bros (Norwich) Ltd**

ISBN 978 07217 1423 3

Target time: **12 minutes**

1. The table shows the results of rolling two dice.

1, 6	2, 2	5, 3	2, 6	3, 4	4, 6
2, 5	1, 1	2, 4	6, 3	5, 2	6, 1
5, 5	3, 1	5, 2	4, 3	2, 1	5, 4
5, 6	2, 4	2, 6	5, 1	3, 3	6, 2
4, 5	5, 3	2, 1	2, 6	6, 3	2, 3

a) Find the difference between the two numbers rolled each time and complete the tally chart.

Difference	Tally	Total
0		
1		
2		
3		
4		
5		

b) Use the information to complete the bar chart below.

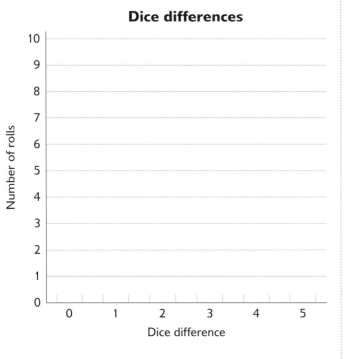

Dice differences

c) Which is the most frequent difference? _____

2. Rita's mum and dad were expecting a baby girl. Rita was trying to choose a name and asked her friends to vote for their favourite.

☺ = 6 votes

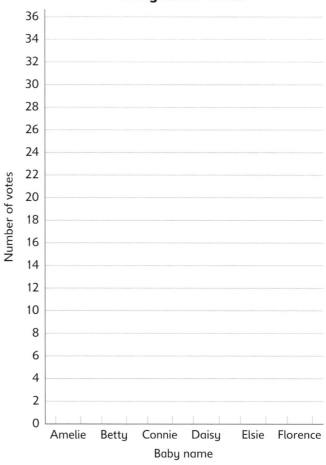

Amelie	☺ ☺ ☺
Betty	☺ ☺ ☺ ☺
Connie	☺ ☺ ☺
Daisy	☺ ☺ ☺ ☺ ☺ ☺
Elsie	☺ ☺
Florence	☺

a) Use the information to complete the bar chart below.

Baby name votes

b) How many children did Rita ask? _____

Score: _____   **Time taken:** _____   **Target met?** _____

Target time: **12 minutes**

1. Solve these calculations.

a)
	5	2
×		5

b)
	6	8
×		9

c)
	7	1
×		8

d)
	5	7
×		7

2. If the following shapes were drawn on cm² paper, what would their areas be?

a)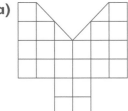

b)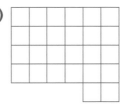

_____ cm²   _____ cm²

3. Write each mass in kilograms.

1100g   100g

a) _____   b) _____

400g   5500g

c) _____   d) _____

4. Find these numbers.

a) What is $\frac{1}{10}$ of 12?   _____

b) What is $\frac{1}{10}$ of 45?   _____

c) What is $\frac{1}{100}$ of 5680?   _____

d) What is $\frac{1}{100}$ of 86?   _____

5. **Benny's bakery**

50p

35p

60p

85p

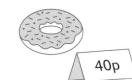
40p

a) Franny bought a loaf of bread and two muffins. How much did she spend?   _____

b) Taylor bought 2 cookies, a hot cross bun and a doughnut. What was her change from £2.   _____

c) Henry had £3. He bought 2 loaves of bread and 2 doughnuts. How much change did he receive?   _____

d) Nathan bought 4 cookies, a muffin and 2 doughnuts. How much did he spend?   _____

e) If I bought one of each item, how much change would I get from £5?   _____

6. A bag of dog treats contains 56 biscuits. Riley buys 8 bags for his dog. How many biscuits will his dog be able to enjoy?   _____

Score: **Time taken:**   **Target met?**

1. Complete the table.

Metres (m)	Fraction (km)	Decimal (km)
1500m	$1\frac{1}{2}$ km	1.5km
2600m		
	$3\frac{7}{10}$ km	
		4.3km

2. How many minutes are there in $2\frac{3}{4}$ hours? _____

3. How many seconds are there in 25 minutes? _____

4. How many days are there in 6 weeks? _____

5. Milo could fit 27 toy cars into each of his toy boxes.

If he filled 7 toy boxes, how many toy cars did he have? _____

6. Solve these fractions sums.

a) $\frac{2}{5} + \frac{1}{5} =$ _____

b) $\frac{5}{12} + \frac{6}{12} =$ _____

c) $\frac{7}{9} - \frac{5}{9} =$ _____

d) $\frac{9}{10} - \frac{4}{10} =$ _____

7. Draw a line to mark each volume.

a)   0.45l   b) $\frac{1}{10}$ l

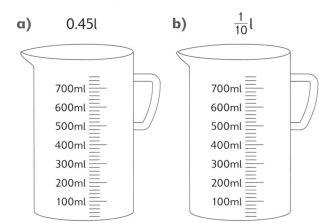

8. Write these numbers in digits.

a) Three thousand, nine hundred and eighteen _____

b) Five thousand, two hundred and fifty-four _____

9. Write this number in words.

8104

_____

_____

10. A supermarket has 894 cans of soup on its shelves.

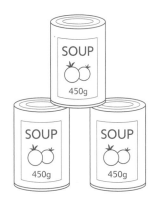

By lunchtime, 564 cans have been sold so 342 more cans are added to the shelves. How many cans of soup are on the shelves now? _____

Score:		Time taken:		Target met?	

Target time: **12 minutes**

1. Solve these calculations.

a)
	3	1	4
×			4

b)
	1	7	9
×			3

c)
	2	7	4
×			6

d)
	2	5	1
×			6

2. George is hosting a BBQ. Burgers come in packets of 8. He buys 65 packets. How many burgers will he have left over if there are 470 people at the BBQ and they each have one burger? _____

3. At a garden centre, there was a display with 238 rose bushes, 467 lavender plants and 297 tulips. How many plants were in the display altogether? _____

4. Nya collected 72 conkers. She found $\frac{5}{8}$ in the park and the rest she found in the school field. How many did she find in the school field? _____

5. A shampoo bottle holds 200ml of shampoo. If Tara uses 20ml each time she washes her hair, how many washes will she get from the bottle? _____

6. Complete these division chains.

a) 270 | ÷ 10 | _____ | ÷ 10 | _____

b) 360 | ÷ 10 | _____ | ÷ 10 | _____

7. Write these times on the 24-hour digital clocks. All these times are in the afternoon or evening.

a)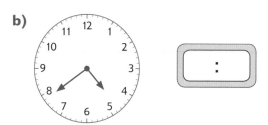

b)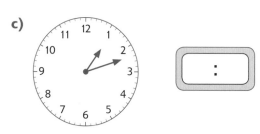

c)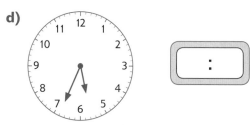

d)

8. Label these angles **acute**, **obtuse** or a **right angle**.

a)  _____

b)  _____

c)  _____

9. Scott walked 300m. $\frac{4}{10}$ of the journey was uphill and the rest was flat. How far did he walk on flat ground? _____

Score:	Time taken:	Target met?

Schofield & Sims

Target time: **12 minutes**

1. This table shows the temperature in Ali's house.

Time	09:00	09:30	10:00	10:30	11:00	11:30
Temp (°C)	18	20	20	15	20	22

a) Use the information to complete the line graph below.

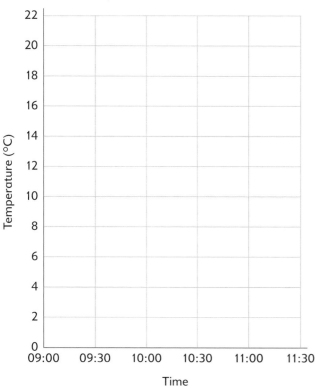

Temperature in Ali's house

b) At what time was it the warmest? _____

c) Estimate the temperature at 09:15. _____

d) Ali has central heating. At what time did he switch it off? _____

2. Leon wants to make some cupcakes but needs 1.7kg of flour. He has 0.8kg in the cupboard and his friend Alex brings round another 400g. How much more flour does he need in grams? _____

3. Convert these measurements.

a) 8.9l = _____ ml

b) 2750ml = _____ l

c) 1250m = _____ km

d) 11.8km = _____ m

e) 3.6kg = _____ g

f) 4250g = _____ kg

4. Ten bagels cost £6.50. How much does one bagel cost? _____

5. Three vertices of a rectangle have been plotted on the grid.

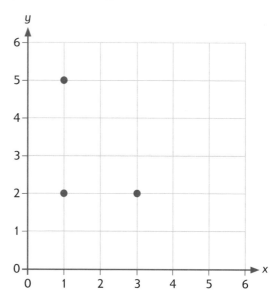

What are the coordinates of the final vertex?

(_____, _____)

6. Max and Jeremy go to the movies. The film they watch is 2 hours and 15 minutes long. The film finishes at 4:30 p.m. At what time did it start? _____

7. There are 96 children in Year 4 and they each need a pencil. Pencils come in boxes of 8. How many boxes of pencils does their teacher need to buy? _____

Score:		Time taken:		Target met?	

Target time: **12 minutes**

1. Write the missing numbers.

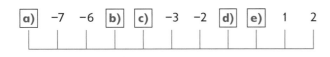

a) _____   b) _____

c) _____   d) _____

e) _____

2. Round these decimals to the nearest 100.

a) 975 _____

b) 9501 _____

3. A fish tank can hold 48 guppies. How many guppies can 6 tanks hold? _____

4. Oliver was 1.34m tall. His cousin Malik was 0.27m shorter. How tall was Malik in metres? _____

5. Eight friendship bracelets cost £3.20. How much would two bracelets cost? _____

6. Reema went shopping and bought 7 packets of stickers, each containing 35 stickers. She then bought 12 individual stickers. How many stickers did she buy altogether? _____

7. Complete these equivalent fractions.

a) $\frac{7}{10} = \frac{?}{100}$ _____

b) $\frac{4}{10} = \frac{?}{5}$ _____

c) $\frac{3}{9} = \frac{?}{3}$ _____

8. How much liquid is in each container?

a)
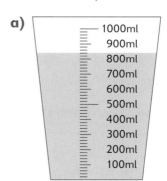
_____ m

b)
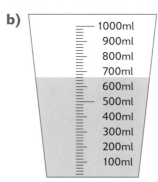
_____

9. Reflect the shape in each of the mirror lines to create a new shape with two lines of symmetry.

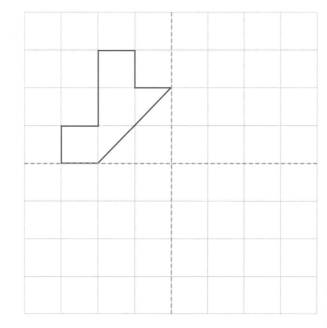

10. How many 10ml helpings are there in a 500ml bottle of tomato ketchup? _____

Target time: **12 minutes**

1. Use this cm² paper to draw a square with a perimeter of 16cm.

2. Round these decimals to the nearest whole number.

a) 1.8 _____

b) 3.9 _____

c) 2.7 _____

3. Solve these calculations.

a) 529 + 736 = _____

b) 602 − 321 = _____

c) 121 × 5 = _____

d) 72 ÷ 8 = _____

4. How many months are there in 4 years? _____

5. The distance between London and Sydney is 16 983km.

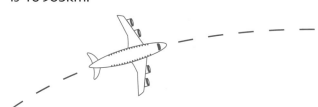

What is this to the nearest 100km? _____

6. Using the map below, find the quickest route between these villages. Write the answers in kilometres.

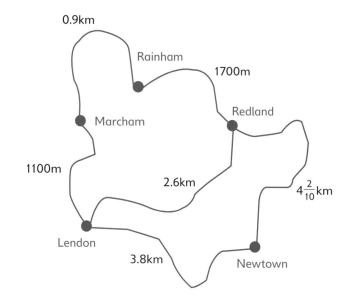

a) Rainham and Newtown _____

b) Marcham and Redland _____

c) Newtown and Marcham _____

d) Rainham and Lendon _____

7. Solve these fractions sums.

a) $\frac{1}{10} + \frac{6}{10} =$ _____

b) $\frac{4}{8} + \frac{3}{8} =$ _____

c) $\frac{12}{16} - \frac{9}{16} =$ _____

d) $\frac{6}{9} - \frac{5}{9} =$ _____

8. Ten friends shared 3 pizzas between them. What fraction did they each get? _____

9. Twelve friends shared 4 cakes between them. What fraction did they each get? _____

Score: _____ **Time taken:** _____ **Target met?** _____

1. Write these numbers in descending order.

   a) 5078   7855   5780   5785   7585

   _____

   b) −12   14   −7   8   2   21   −18

   _____

2. Write these numbers in ascending order.

   a) 3741   3471   3174   3714   3417

   _____

   b) 5   −10   4   15   −24   0   −2

   _____

3. Write these Roman numerals in digits.

   a) CCCLXXII   _____

   b) MCCXXXVIII   _____

4. Complete these sequences.

   a) 15 000, 16 000, _____,

       _____, 19 000

   b) 37 000, _____, 39 000,

       _____, 41 000

   c) 4300, _____, 4100,

       4000, _____

5. What is the value of each underlined digit?

   a) 2<u>9</u>36   _____

   b) <u>9</u>273   _____

6. Latif thinks of a number. All
   the digits are odd. The number
   is larger than 200 but smaller
   than 500. The digits add up to 5.
   What is Latif's number?   _____

7. Write **<** or **>** to make these statements correct.

   a) 2093 _____ 2097

   b) 3130 _____ 3103

8. Round these numbers to the nearest 100 and
   the nearest 1000.

	Nearest 100	Nearest 1000
975	a)	b)
9501	c)	d)

9. Circle the numbers that are multiples of 5.

   18   64

   25   42

   75   30

10. Ayesha has to guess the correct number to
   win a prize. She has been given four clues.

   • There are 4 ones.
   • The hundreds digit is one less than the
     thousands digit.
   • There are twice as many thousands as ones
   • There are 6 tens.

   What is the number?   _____

Score: _____   Time taken: _____   Target met? _____

Target time: **12 minutes**

1. Solve these calculations.

   a) 7 − 9 = _____

   b) 4 − 8 = _____

   c) 648 + 456 = _____

   d) 975 − 685 = _____

2. There were 246 apartments in one building and twice as many in another building on the other side of the street.

   How many homes were
   there altogether? _____

3. A local beekeeper had 527 bees.

   Three hundred and seventeen
   of them were out looking for
   pollen. How many were left
   in the hive? _____

4. Complete these function machines.

   a) 16 → | × 2 | → | − 11 | = _____

   b) 25 → | ÷ 5 | → | + 12 | = _____

   c) _____ → | × 3 | → | + 17 | = 41

5. Solve these calculations.

   a)
	3	1	4
×			4

   b)
	1	7	9
×			3

   c)
	2	7	4
×			6

   d)
	2	5	1
×			6

   e) 121 ÷ _____ = 11

   f) _____ ÷ 4 = 12

   g) _____ ÷ 8 = 9

   h) 144 ÷ _____ = 12

6. A train carriage had 124 seats.
   If there were 6 carriages on the
   train, how many seats were there
   on the train altogether? _____

7. Write the two factor pairs for
   the number 51.

   a) _____ and _____

   b) _____ and _____

Target time: **12 minutes**

1. Find these numbers.

a) What is $\frac{3}{4}$ of 12? _____

b) What is $\frac{3}{10}$ of 40? _____

c) What is $\frac{5}{8}$ of 24? _____

d) What is $\frac{3}{5}$ of 40? _____

2. Complete these equivalent fractions.

a) $\frac{4}{12} = \frac{?}{3}$ _____

b) $\frac{6}{15} = \frac{?}{5}$ _____

3. There were 77 sheep in a field. $\frac{2}{11}$ were lambs. How many were adult sheep? _____

4. Roxy counted 36 butterflies in her garden.

$\frac{2}{6}$ were red admiral butterflies and the rest were cabbage whites. How many cabbage whites did she spot? _____

5. Write the missing fractions.

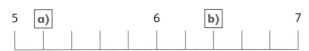

a) _____   b) _____

6. Write the missing decimals.

a) _____   b) _____

7. Look at these number cards.

a) Using these cards, make six 3-digit numbers to two decimal places.

_____ _____ _____

_____ _____ _____

b) Write them in ascending order.

_____

8. The tree at the bottom of Hasan's garden was 6.7m tall. His dad cut 1.8m off the top. How tall was the tree after this? _____

9. Complete these sequences.

a) 0.3, 0.4, 0.5, 0.6, _____, _____

b) 1.23, 1.24, 1.25, _____, _____

10. Fern ran 100m in 12.4 seconds. Hattie ran it 1.3 seconds slower. What was Hattie's time? _____

11. Hanna saved $\frac{3}{4}$ of her money and spent the rest. If she spent £1.50, how much did she save? _____

12. Amy cycled for 8.7km before turning round and cycling the same distance home. How far had she cycled altogether? _____

Score: _____   Time taken: _____   Target met? _____

Target time: **12 minutes**

1. The following shape is drawn on cm² paper. What is its area? _____

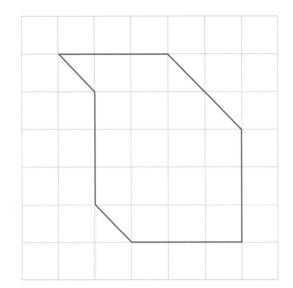

2. How many days are there in a leap year? _____

3. How many days are there in a fortnight? _____

4. How many seconds are there in 5 minutes? _____

5. Write these times on the 24-hour digital clocks. Both of these times are in the morning.

a)

b)
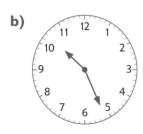

6. Kamal needs £48 to buy a ticket for the football match. He only has £27.50. How much more money does he need? _____

7. How many 20p coins are there in £5? _____

8. How many 10p coins are there in £1.50? _____

9. Oranges cost 52p a kilo and apples cost 38p a kilo. I buy half a kilo of apples and a kilo of oranges. What is my change from £1? _____

10. A parcel contains a book weighing 800g, a puzzle weighing 0.6kg, a fruitcake weighing 1.2kg and a calendar weighing 200g. If the box's maximum weight is 3.5kg, how much weight can still be added? _____

11. Write these capacities in litres using decimal notation.

a)	b)	c)	d)	e)
Apple juice	Water	Cola	Milk	Lemonade
250ml	500ml	330ml	150ml	850ml

a) _____   b) _____

c) _____   d) _____

e) _____

Which two drinks can be added together to make the following capacities?

f) 1l _____

g) 580ml _____

h) 0.65l _____

i) 1.35l _____

Score:		Time taken:		Target met?	

Target time: **12 minutes**

1. Reflect the shape in each of the mirror lines to create a new shape with two lines of symmetry.

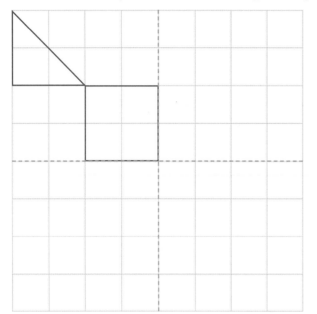

2. Translate this shape 3 squares to the left and 1 square down.

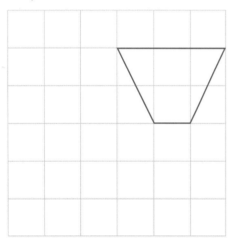

3. How many acute angles in these shapes?

a) _____ b) _____ c) _____

4. How many obtuse angles in these shapes?

a) _____ b) _____ c) _____

5. a) Plot these coordinates and join them.

(2, 1)   (3, 3)   (2, 6)   (1, 3)

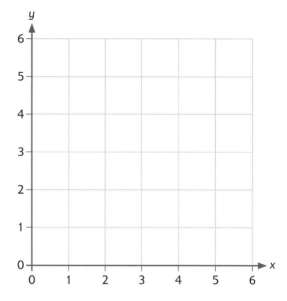

b) Name the shape you have plotted.

_____

6. I have 5 faces, 8 edges and 5 vertices. What shape am I?

_____

7. I have one curved face and 2 circular faces. What shape am I?

_____

8. Draw the lines of symmetry on these shapes.

a)    b)

c)

Score: _____   Time taken: _____   Target met? _____

Target time: **12 minutes**

. The tally chart below shows the favourite ice cream flavours of children at Highbeam School.

a) Complete the tally chart.

Flavour	Tally	Total
Vanilla	卌 卌 卌 卌 卌 II	
Chocolate	卌 卌 卌 卌 II	
Strawberry	卌 卌 卌 III	
Coconut	卌 II	
Pistachio	卌 卌	
Mint	卌 卌 I	

b) Use the information to complete the bar chart below.

Favourite ice cream

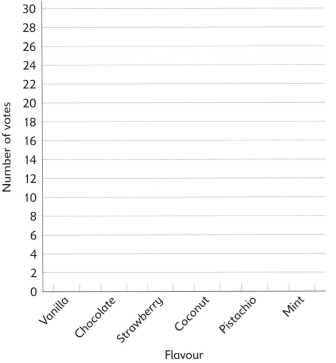

c) How many more people voted for strawberry ice cream than coconut? _____

d) Which ice cream was twice as popular as mint ice cream?

_____

e) Which was the third most popular ice cream?

_____

f) How many children voted? _____

2. The line graph below shows the temperatures over a seven-day period in December.

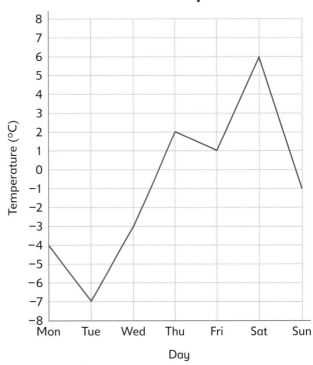

a) On which day did the temperature rise above freezing?

_____

b) What was the difference in temperature between Wednesday and Thursday? _____

c) Between which two days was there the biggest drop in temperature?

_____

d) On how many days was the temperature above freezing? _____

Score:		Time taken:		Target met?	

1. Write the coordinates of the pentagon.

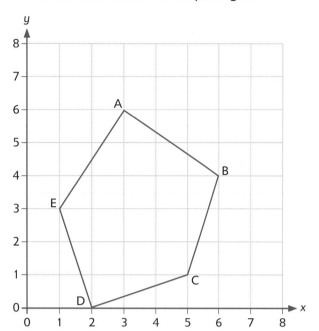

a) A = (_____ , _____)

b) B = (_____ , _____)

c) C = (_____ , _____)

d) D = (_____ , _____)

e) E = (_____ , _____)

2. Ben left 1.3l of water for his dog, Pippa. Pippa drank some of the water but left 250ml. How much water did she drink in litres? _____

3. Chocolate bars cost 26p each.

a) How many bars can I buy for £2? _____

b) What will my change be? _____

4. Gemma tries to carry a full litre jug of water to the table. She spills 0.28l on the way. How many millilitres of water are still in the jug? _____

5. A fishmonger was weighing the fish in his shop. He had two pieces of cod weighing 200g each, 3 trout weighing 0.3kg each and a whole salmon that weighed 1.4kg. What was the total mass of his fish? _____

6. Write these numbers in digits.

   a) Seven thousand, six hundred and nine _____

   b) Nine thousand and six _____

7. Write **<** or **>** to make these statements correct

   a) 9.37 _____ 9.73

   b) 10.84 _____ 10.48

   c) −7 _____ −12

8. Mikey and Michelle go for a run. They set off at 11:30 a.m. and run for 50 minutes. At what time do they stop running? _____

9. Round these numbers to the nearest 1000.

   a) 5612 _____

   b) 3501 _____

   c) 1334 _____

10. There were 36 children in Remi's class. Three-quarters had brown hair. How many children had brown hair? _____

Score: _____   Time taken: _____   Target met? _____

Target time: **12 minutes**

1. Lana put bottles in the garden to collect rainwater.

   Bottle A collected 230ml. Bottle B collected twice as much as Bottle A, and Bottle C collected twice as much as Bottle B.

   How many litres of rainwater did Lana collect? _____

2. Complete the conversion chart.

Millilitres (ml)	Litres (l) and millilitres (ml)	Decimal (l)	Fraction (l)
400ml	0l 400ml	0.4l	$\frac{4}{10}$l
1200ml		1.2l	
	2l 700ml		$2\frac{7}{10}$l
3600ml			

3. Dolly bought a bag of buttons weighing 1.3kg, which she wanted to use for her craft projects.

   By the end of the first week she had used 0.2kg. By the end of the second week she had used a further 400g and by the end of the third week she had used a further 250g.

   What was the mass in grams of buttons that she had left at the end of the third week? _____

4. Convert these times from the 12-hour clock to the 24-hour clock.

   a) 7:42 pm   [:]

   b) 4:38 am   [:]

5. Florence and Lainey want to go swimming.

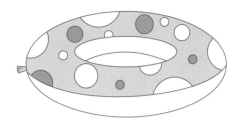

   The pool does not open until 9:30 a.m. and it is currently 8:15 a.m. How many minutes do they have to wait? _____

6. The perimeter of an equilateral triangle was 18cm. How long was each side? _____

7. There were 45 chocolates in a box. $\frac{2}{5}$ were milk chocolate, $\frac{1}{5}$ were dark chocolate and the rest were white chocolate. How many were white chocolate? _____

8. Solve these fractions sums.

   a) $\frac{4}{12} + \frac{5}{12} =$ _____

   b) $\frac{3}{4} - \frac{1}{4} =$ _____

   c) $\frac{8}{13} - \frac{4}{13} =$ _____

9. Satish shares 108 pencils between 12 pencil pots. Two pencils in each pot then get lost. How many pencils are now in each pot? _____

10. Solve these Roman numeral calculations. Write the answers in Roman numerals.

   a) XXI + XLI = _____

   b) XC + XXVI = _____

Score: [ ]   **Time taken:** [ ]   **Target met?** [ ]

Target time: **12 minutes**

1. A school had a 'Guess the weight of the marbles' competition. The scale below shows the guesses.

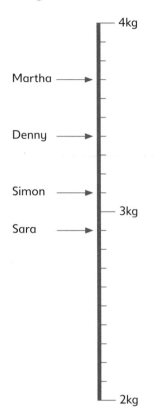

a) Complete the table showing each child's guess, then round each to the nearest kilogram.

Child	Guessed mass (kg)	Nearest kilogram
Martha		
Denny		
Simon		
Sara		

b) The actual weight was 3.2kg. Whose guess was the closest?

_____

2. My best friend went to Paris for 28 days. How many weeks was she gone for? _____

3. Solve these calculations.

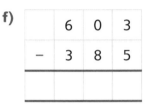

a)
	3	0	9
×			8

b)
	4	0	2
×			7

c)
	6	2	7
+	5	3	9

d)
	8	6	8
+	4	2	3

e)
	3	7	6
−	1	8	9

f)
	6	0	3
−	3	8	5

4. Lara was clearing out her bedroom. She filled 6 plastic bags with a total of 48 pieces of clothing. If there were the same number of items in each bag, how many pieces of clothing were in each bag? _____

5. Riya went shopping with 80p. She spent $\frac{3}{4}$ on a toy plane and saved the rest. How much did she save? _____

6. Write these decimals in descending order.

1.62   1.26   2.61   6.12   6.21

_____

7. Write these decimals in ascending order.

5.51   1.55   5.15   5.05   5.5

_____

Score:		Time taken:		Target met?	

Target time: **12 minutes**

. Complete these division chains.

a) 510 | ÷ 10 | _____ | ÷ 10 | _____

b) _____ | ÷ 10 | _____ | ÷ 10 | 7.5

. Gauri and Hena were making a scarf each.

Gauri knitted a scarf that was
1.2m long. Hena's scarf was
0.5m shorter. How long was
Hena's scarf in metres?   _____

3. Betty's younger sister spent 24.7
seconds tying her left shoelace
and 22.5 seconds tying her right
shoelace. How long did it take
her to tie both shoelaces?   _____

4. The following shape is drawn on
cm² paper. Estimate its area.   _____

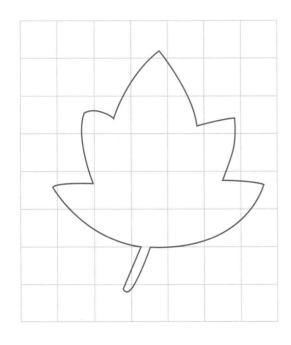

5. The height of the Empire State
Building in New York is 443m.
What is this to the nearest 10m?   _____

6. Dylan's school building was
24m tall. How tall was it
in centimetres?   _____

7. Solve these calculations.

a) £3.82 + £0.97 =   _____

b) £4.15 + £2.74 =   _____

c) £5.28 − £3.15 =   _____

d) £6.93 − £3.61 =   _____

8. If one can of lemonade holds
250ml, how much will 7 cans
hold? Write the answer in litres.   _____

9. Write these numbers in words.

a) 9086

_____

_____

b) 13906

_____

_____

10. Eight friends shared
5 doughnuts. What
fraction did they
each get?

     _____

11. Write **<** or **>** to make these statements correct.

a) 3.93 _____ 3.39

b) 6.91 _____ 6.19

c) 12.12 _____ 12.21

| Score: | | Time taken: | | Target met? | |

Target time: **12 minutes**

1. Look at these weighing scales.

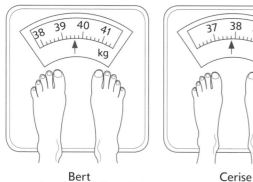

Bert   Cerise

a) How much does Bert weigh? _____

b) How much does Cerise weigh? _____

c) How much more does
Bert weigh? _____

2. Bottles of olive oil come in two
different sizes, 200ml and 500ml.
If a restaurant bought 8 of the
smaller bottles and 5 of the
larger bottles, how many litres
of olive oil would they have? _____

3. Thomas gives Mike his 350ml
carton of apple juice. Mike's
friend Jarrad then gives him
the remaining half a carton
of his apple juice. How much
apple juice does Mike have? _____

4. There were 1.8kg of biscuits
in the biscuit jar. Ava took half
for her and her friends and then
Adam came and took some for
him and his friends. There are
now only 200g of biscuits left.
What mass did Adam take? _____

5. Solve these calculations.

a) $37 \times 7 =$ _____

b) $4219 + 3175 =$ _____

c) $6342 - 1428 =$ _____

6. **a)** Plot these coordinates and join them
to make a shape with two pairs of
parallel lines.

(0, 4)   (6, 6)   (2, 6)   (4, 4)

b) Name the shape you have plotted.

_____

7. Convert these measurements.

a) $12\,750g =$ _____ kg

b) $1050cm =$ _____ m

c) $11\,200m =$ _____ km

d) $4250ml =$ _____ l

8. Serena swam 800m. She swam
breaststroke for $\frac{2}{10}$ of the way,
backstroke for $\frac{3}{10}$ of the way
and for the rest she swam front
crawl. How far did she swim
front crawl? _____

9. What is $\frac{3}{12}$ of 144? _____

Score: _____   **Time taken:** _____   **Target met?** _____

Target time: **12 minutes**

. Write these numbers in Roman numerals.

a) 47 _____

b) 71 _____

c) 129 _____

d) 456 _____

2. The table below shows the dimensions of a small hill.

Distance across hill	0m	0.5m	1m	1.5m	2m	2.5m	3m
Height of hill	0m	0.2m	0.5m	1.3m	1.4m	0.7m	0m

a) Use the information to complete the line graph below.

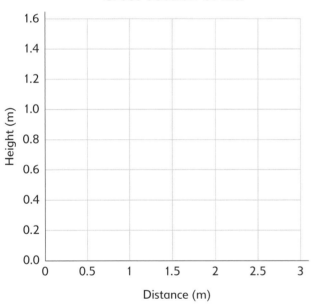

Cross section of hill

b) Approximately how high is the hill at 0.25m across? _____

c) Between which two distances does the height rise by the most? _____

3. Oscar drew a line that was 55mm long. He then made it 75mm longer. How long is his line in centimetres? _____

4. It takes Suzanne 240 seconds to cycle around her garden. How many minutes does it take her to cycle twice around her garden? _____

5. A cricket match started at 11:40 a.m. It lasted 3 hours and 40 minutes. At what time did it end?  _____

6. Fluffy the cat knocked over his box of cat food.

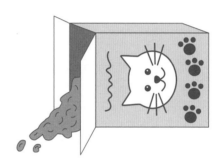

0.3kg fell on the floor and was eaten straight away. There was then 0.5kg left in the box. What was the mass in grams before Fluffy knocked over the box? _____

7. Anita gets £12 for her birthday, saves £4.50 of her pocket money and finds £1.25 behind the sofa. How much money does she have? _____

8. Write the missing decimals.

2   a)   b) 4

a) _____   b) _____

Progress chart

Write the score (out of 20) for each test in the box provided on the right of the graph.
Then colour in the row next to the box to represent this score.

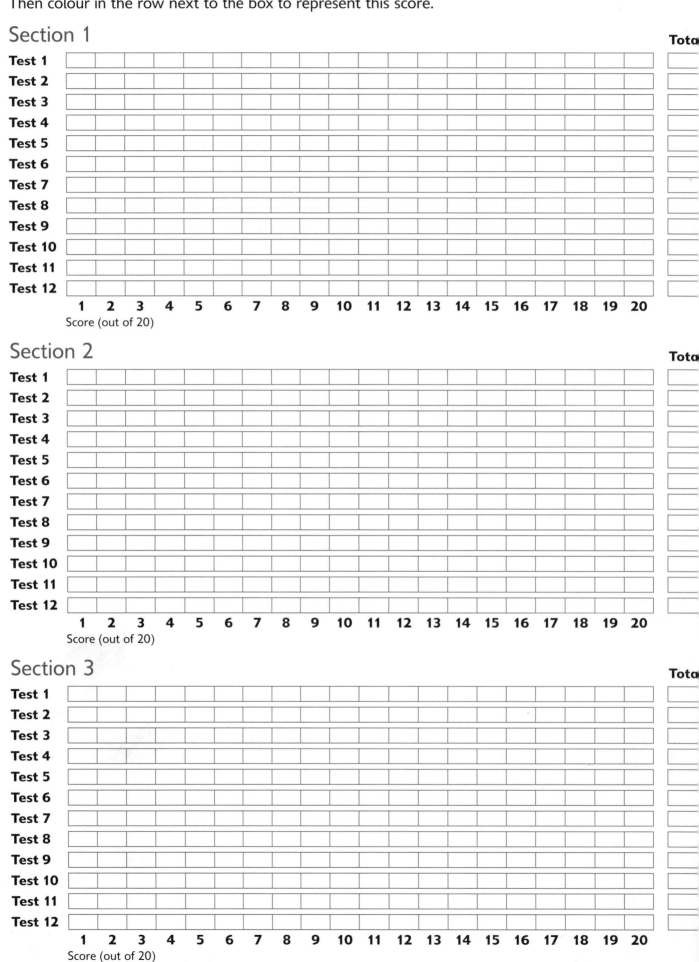

Section 1

Total

	1	2	3	4	5	6	7	8	9	10	11	12	13	14	15	16	17	18	19	20
Test 1																				
Test 2																				
Test 3																				
Test 4																				
Test 5																				
Test 6																				
Test 7																				
Test 8																				
Test 9																				
Test 10																				
Test 11																				
Test 12																				

Score (out of 20)

Section 2

Total

	1	2	3	4	5	6	7	8	9	10	11	12	13	14	15	16	17	18	19	20
Test 1																				
Test 2																				
Test 3																				
Test 4																				
Test 5																				
Test 6																				
Test 7																				
Test 8																				
Test 9																				
Test 10																				
Test 11																				
Test 12																				

Score (out of 20)

Section 3

Total

	1	2	3	4	5	6	7	8	9	10	11	12	13	14	15	16	17	18	19	20
Test 1																				
Test 2																				
Test 3																				
Test 4																				
Test 5																				
Test 6																				
Test 7																				
Test 8																				
Test 9																				
Test 10																				
Test 11																				
Test 12																				

Score (out of 20)